Laboratory Manual to accompany

DATA AND TELECOMMUNICATIONS
Systems and Applications

Charles N. Thurwachter, Jr.
DeVry Institute of Technology

Prentice Hall

Upper Saddle River, New Jersey   Columbus, Ohio

Publisher: Charles E. Stewart, Jr.
Associate Editor: Kate Linsner
Production Editor: Rachel S. Besen
Design Coordinator: Karrie Converse-Jones
Cover Designer: Thomas Mack
Production Manager: Matt Ottenweller
Marketing Manager: Ben Leonard

This book was set in Times by Prentice Hall and was printed and bound by The Banta Company. The cover was printed by Phoenix Color Corp.

Printed in the United States of America

10 9 8 7 6 5 4 3 2 1

ISBN: 0-13-793928-0

Prentice-Hall International (UK) Limited, *London*
Prentice-Hall of Australia Pty. Limited, *Sydney*
Prentice-Hall of Canada, Inc., *Toronto*
Prentice-Hall Hispanoamericana, S. A., *Mexico*
Prentice-Hall of India Private Limited, *New Delhi*
Prentice-Hall of Japan, Inc., *Tokyo*
Prentice-Hall (Singapore) Pte. Ltd., *Singapore*
Editora Prentice-Hall do Brasil, Ltda., *Rio de Janeiro*

Preface

This laboratory manual features 20 experiments, broken down into five groups:

1) 11 are traditional protoboard based electronics experiments

2) 2 are purely instrument-based experiments involving no protoboard wiring

3) 1 is a circuit simulation using Electronics Workbench which can be easily adapted to protoboard

4) 2 are paper-based exercises in coding

5) 4 are networking simulations using the COMNET III network simulator

These laboratory exercises are tied to the instructional themes of the textbook. The table below indicates the chapter association by experiment number.

I	Voltage Controlled Oscillator	Chapter 8
II	Duty Cycle Exploration	Chapter 6
III	Phase Locked Loop	Chapter 8
IV	Harmonic Content Exploration	Chapter 6
V	Further Harmonic Analysis	Chapter 6
VI	AM DSB-LC Modulator	Chapter 8
VII	AM Envelope Detector	Chapter 8
VIII	FM Modulator	Chapter 9
IX	FM Demodulator	Chapter 9
X	PCM CODEC/COMBO	Chapter 10
XI	Huffman Codes	Chapter 12
XII	Code Trees	Chapter 12
XIII	BFSK Modulator	Chapter 13
XIV	BFSK Demodulator	Chapter 13
XV	Pulse Width Modulation	Chapter 10
XVI	CRC Codes	Chapter 12
XVII	COMNET III – Introduction	Chapters 14 & 15
XVIII	COMNET III – LAN/WAN	Chapters 14 & 15
XIX	COMNET III – Ethernet Collisions	Chapters 14 & 15
XX	COMNET III – Modem Pool	Chapter 16

Contents

Experiment I Voltage Controlled Oscillator

Primary: _____   Assistant: _____

Signature: _____

Introductory Discussion:

This experiment will explore the operation of a voltage controlled oscillator (VCO). Fundamentally, a VCO converts a voltage or current into a frequency. This experiment is composed of two sections. The first section will use the Binary Keying Inputs to select four output frequencies. In the second section, a variable voltage supply will be used to adjust the output frequency continuously.

Parts List:

IC1	1 – XR-2207 Voltage Controlled Oscillator
Ct	1 – 0.1 µF non-polarized Timing Capacitor
Ct	1 – 0.01µF non-polarized Timing Capacitor
Cb	2 – 0.1 µF Bypass Capacitor
Rp	3 – 20 kΩ Pull-up Resistor
R1	1 – 20 kΩ Resistor
R2	1 – 20 kΩ Resistor
R3	1 – 5.1 kΩ Resistor
R4	1 – 5.1 kΩ Resistor
Rc	1 – 1 kΩ Resistor
Re	1 – 1 MΩ Resistor
S1	1 – SPST Switch
S2	1 – SPST Switch

Power Supply Specifications:

Vcc	+8 V Positive Supply
Vee	−8 V Negative Supply

Integrated Circuit Pin Description:

1	Vcc	Positive Supply
2	CT	Timing Capacitor Input
3	CT	Timing Capacitor Input
4	R1	Timing Resistor 1 Input
5	R2	Timing Resistor 2 Input
6	R3	Timing Resistor 3 Input
7	R4	Timing Resistor 4 Input
8	BKI1	Binary Keying 1 Timing Resistor Select Input
9	BKI2	Binary Keying 2 Timing Resistor Select Input
10	GND	Ground
11	Bias	Bias Input (use for single supply operation only)
12	Vee	Negative Supply
13	SWO	Square Wave Output
14	TWO	Triangle Wave Output

Functional Block Diagram:

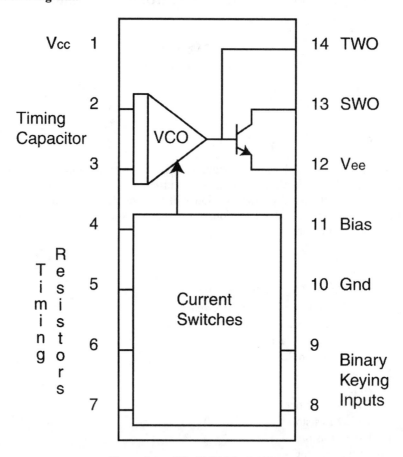

Figure I.1 – XR-2207 Block Diagram

Operational Overview:

The XR-2207 is composed of two primary functional blocks. The first is the voltage controlled oscillator (VCO) itself. As discussed in the text, a VCO is a device that converts a voltage into a frequency. The XR-2207 VCO is implemented as a multivibrator; like any multivibrator its frequency of operation is set by the timing resistor and timing capacitor.

A typical multivibrator, like the 556 timer, has a set frequency of operation determined by the timing resistor and capacitor. The XR-2207 modifies this set frequency of operation into a variable frequency of operation by allowing the user to control the current flow through the resistor. This allows a familiar device to be used as a VCO.

The second primary function block are the four current switches controlled by the two binary keying inputs. Through this use of the binary keying inputs one or two of the timing resistors can be selected. By varying the value of the resistor, the current flow is varied and hence the output frequency of the VCO is varied.

The XR-2207 has two outputs; pin 13 is the SWO or Square Wave Output and pin 14 is the TWO or Triangle Wave Output. Note that the SWO is an open collector output and must be pulled up by a resistor to Vcc.

Section 1:

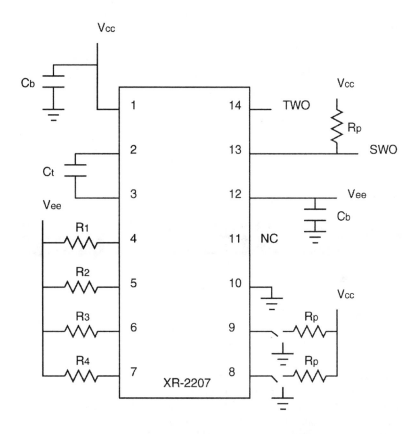

Figure I.2 – Section 1: schematic

Procedure:

In this section, the current flow will be varied and hence the frequency of oscillation by using the binary keying switches to select the four possible combinations of resistors the XR-2207 permits.

1) Connect the circuit shown in Figure I.2. Use the 0.1 µF for Ct.

2) Fill in the calculation column of Table I.1 using equations I-1.

$$f_1 = \frac{1}{C_t R_3} \quad \Delta f_1 = \frac{1}{C_t R_4} \quad f_2 = \frac{1}{C_t R_2} \quad \Delta f_2 = \frac{1}{C_t R_1} \qquad (I\text{-}1)$$

Pin 8	Pin 9	Timing Pin(s) Selected	Output Frequency Formula	Output Frequency Calculated	Output Frequency Measured
0	0	6	F1		
0	1	6 & 7	F1 + ΔF1		
1	0	5	F2		
1	1	4 & 5	F2 + ΔF2		

Table I.1 0.1µF Timing Capacitor

3

3) Apply the SWO output to the input of your oscilloscope. Measure the frequency observed for each of the setting for the binary keying switches. Fill in the output frequency measured column of table I.1.

4) Repeat step 3 using the TWO output and verify the same measured frequency. Record the measured results in the space below.

F1 _____ F1 + ΔF1 _____ F2 _____ F2 + ΔF2 _____

Were the measured frequencies the same? _____

5) Exchange Ct for the 0.01μF capacitor and repeat step 2 and 3. Fill in table I.2.

Pin 8	Pin 9	Timing Pin(s) Selected	Output Frequency Formula	Output Frequency Calculated	Output Frequency Measured
0	0	6	F1		
0	1	6 & 7	F1 + ΔF1		
1	0	5	F2		
1	1	4 & 5	F2 + ΔF2		

Table I.2 0.01μF Timing Capacitor

6) Plot the results from both tables using the Excel spreadsheet graphing function. Use one graph to display both sets of results. Show the total resistance value of each measured point on the horizontal axis and the frequency measured for that resistance value on the vertical axis. Make a note of the dependence of output frequency on the value of the Timing Capacitance and Timing Resistance. This will help you answer questions 2 and 3.

Section 2:

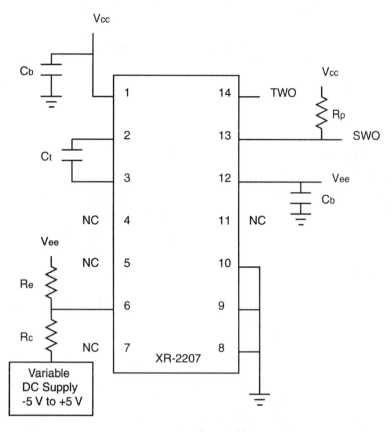

Figure I.3 – XR-2207 Schematic

Procedure:

1)   Connect the circuit shown in Figure I.3.   Use the 0.1μF for Ct.

2)   Set the voltage on the variable DC supply to –5 V. Connect the oscilloscope to the TWO output.   Measure the output frequency and record in the table below.   Repeat this measurement and recording for 1 V steps to + 5 V.

Applied DC Voltage	Output Frequency Measured
– 5	
– 4	
– 3	
– 2	
– 1	
0	
+ 1	
+ 2	
+ 3	
+ 4	
+ 5	

Table I.3

5

3)   Plot the results from table I.3 using the Excel spreadsheet graphing function. Show the DC voltage applied on the horizontal axis and the frequency measured on the vertical axis. Make a note of the relationship between the applied voltage and the output frequency. This will help you in answering question 4.

4)   Swap the variable DC supply for a function generator. Set the function generator as follows:

Output Waveform: Sinusoidal
Frequency: 1 Hz
Voltage: 4 V peak-to-peak
DC Offset: − 2.5 V

5)   Observe the TWO output on the oscilloscope. Note how the frequency of the waveform is changing. Record the maximum and minimum frequencies observed. Be careful, you will need to make these measurements manually, do not attempt to use an automatic measurement.

Maximum _____   Minimum _____

6)   Explain what you are seeing; why is the frequency of the output waveform changing? Examine table I.3 for a clue. Record your answer on the lines below.

_____

_____

_____

_____

7)   Change the function generator to a square wave output. Note the difference in the behavior of the TWO output waveform. Record your observations on the lines below.

_____

_____

_____

_____

8)   Change the DC offset of the function generator to + 2.5 V. Observe the TWO output. Why does the output now appear stationary? Examine table I.3 closely for a clue. Record your answer on the lines below.

_____

_____

_____

_____

Questions:

1) Describe the basic operation of a VCO.

2) Using the results from section 1, describe the dependence of output frequency on applied timing resistance.

3) Using the results from section 1, describe the dependence of output frequency on applied timing capacitance.

4) Using the results from section 2, describe the dependence of output frequency on applied voltage. How did the results change as the applied DC voltage changed polarity? Why did this occur?

5) Using the results from section 2, describe the dependence of output frequency on applied current.

Experiment II Duty Cycle Exploration

Primary: _____   Assistant: _____

Signature: _____

Introductory Discussion:

This experiment will explore the concept of duty cycle of a waveform. The duty cycle of a pulsed waveform will be varied. Measurements will be performed to illustrate how the harmonic content of a pulsed waveform changes as a function of duty cycle.

Parts List:

IC1	1 – XR-2207 Voltage Controlled Oscillator
Ct	1 – 0.1 µF non-polarized Timing Capacitor
Cb	2 – 0.1 µF Bypass Capacitor
Rp	1 – 20 kΩ Pull-up Resistor
R1	1 – 1 kΩ Resistor
R1	1 – 2.2 kΩ Resistor
R1	1 – 3.3 kΩ Resistor
R1	1 – 4.7 kΩ Resistor
R1	1 – 6.8 kΩ Resistor
R1	1 – 10 kΩ Resistor
R1	1 – 15 kΩ Resistor
R2	1 – 20 kΩ Variable Resistor (10-turn)

Power Supply Specifications:

Vcc	+8 V Positive Supply
Vee	−8 V Negative Supply

Integrated Circuit Pin Description:

1	Vcc	Positive Supply
2	C1	Timing Capacitor Input
3	C2	Timing Capacitor Input
4	R1	Timing Resistor 1 Input
5	R2	Timing Resistor 2 Input
6	R3	Timing Resistor 3 Input
7	R4	Timing Resistor 4 Input
8	BKI1	Binary Keying 1 Timing Resistor Select Input
9	BKI2	Binary Keying 2 Timing Resistor Select Input
10	GND	Ground
11	Bias	Bias Input (use for single supply operation only)
12	Vee	Negative Supply
13	SWO	Square Wave Output
14	TWO	Triangle Wave Output

Functional Block Diagram:

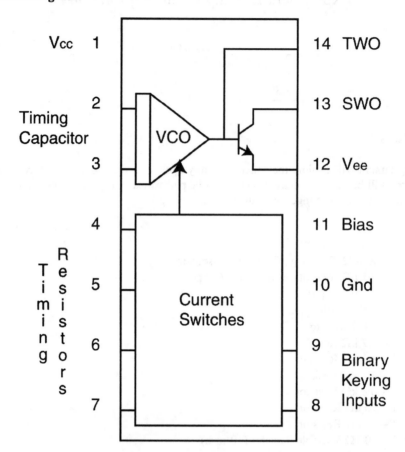

Figure II.1 – XR-2207 Block Diagram

Operational Overview:

The XR-2207 functional description can be found in Experiment I. This experiment uses the integrated circuit in a new way. By connecting the output of one of the Binary Keying Pins, 8 or 9, back to the SWO when the square wave pulses high, it simulates a frequency selection toggle. In this experiment the frequency selection will be used to effect a duty cycle toggle.

The frequency of oscillation of the VCO is determined by the sum of the two resistor values connected to pins 5 and 6. This sum will be held constant throughout the experiment. The duty cycle is determined by the ratio of one of the resistors to their sum, and this ratio will be varied. Through this approach, a variable duty cycle waveform will be obtained at a constant frequency. In this manner using both time domain and frequency domain analysis, the effect of duty cycle on waveform shape and frequency content will be explored.

Duty cycle and frequency are unrelated. Taking T1 as the active part of a pulse and T2 as the period of the pulse, duty cycle and frequency are generally defined as shown in equation II-1.

$$ DC = \frac{T_1}{T_2} \qquad\qquad f = \frac{1}{T_2} \quad \text{(II-1)} $$

Section 1:

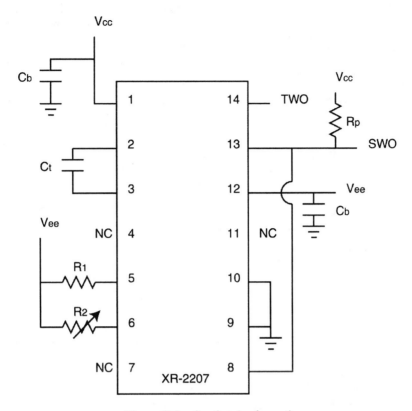

Figure II.2 – Section 1 schematic

Procedure:

1) Connect the circuit shown in Figure II.2. Use the 1 kΩ resistor for R1. Adjust R2 to full scale (10 kΩ). Use a multimeter to record the actual resistance of R1 and R2. Record your results below. Also record the sum of R1 and R2 in the second column of row 1 of table II.1.

R1 = _____   R2 = _____

2) Connect the oscilloscope to pin 13 and measure the duty cycle and output frequency and record below. Print out the waveform observed.

1.0 kΩ DC = _____   f = _____

3) Substitute the 2.2 kΩ resistor for R1. Again use a multimeter to record the actual value of R1. Then adjust R2 such that the sum of R1 and R2 have the same result as measured in step 1. Record this in table II.1. Use the oscilloscope and record the duty cycle and output frequency measured on pin 13 below. Print out the waveform observed.

R1 = _____   R2 = _____

2.2 kΩ DC = _____   f = _____

11

4) Repeat step 3 for the other values of R1, namely, 3.3 kΩ, 4.7 kΩ, and 6.8 kΩ. Print out the waveform observed on pin 13 for each case and record the frequency and results below. Also record the sum of R1 and R2 in table II.1 Make sure the sum of resistances stays the same as measured in step 1.

R1 = _____   R2 = _____

3.3 kΩ DC = _____   f = _____

R1 = _____   R2 = _____

4.7 kΩ DC = _____   f = _____

R1 = _____   R2 = _____

6.8 kΩ DC = _____   f = _____

R1 = _____   R2 = _____

10 kΩ   DC = _____   f = _____

R1 = _____   R2 = _____

15 kΩ   DC = _____   f = _____

5) Calculate the duty cycle and output frequency for each of the resistor combinations using equations II-2. Record your results in table II.1.

$$DC = \frac{R_1}{R_1 + R_2} \qquad f = \frac{2}{C_t}\left[\frac{1}{R_1 + R_2}\right] \qquad (\text{II - 2})$$

R1	R1 + R2	Duty Cycle	Frequency
1.0 kΩ			
2.2 kΩ			
3.3 kΩ			
4.7 kΩ			
6.8 kΩ			
10 kΩ			
15 kΩ			

Table II.1

6)   Connect a spectrum analyzer or the FFT input to your oscilloscope to pin 13. Set the frequency domain instrument as follows:

Units/Division:	10 dB
Reference Level:	10 dBV
Center Frequency:	50 kHz
Frequency Span:	~100 kHz
Window:	Hanning

For each of the resistor combinations used above, print out the results. Make sure to adjust R2 for each new value of R1, so that the sum of the two resistors is constant. Print out the display for each value of R1. Record the <u>amplitude</u> in decibels of the fundamental and first few harmonics for each value of R1 in Table II.2.

R1	Fundamental Frequency Amplitude	2nd Harmonic	3rd Harmonic	4th Harmonic	5th Harmonic	6th Harmonic	7th Harmonic
1 k							
2.2 k							
3.3 k							
4.7 k							
6.8 k							
10 k							
15 k							

Table II.2

7)   Plot the results using the Excel spreadsheet tool. On the horizontal axis show the value of R1 and on the vertical axis show the amplitude of the 2nd, 3rd and 4th harmonics. Use one graph to display all the data.

Questions:

1)   Define duty cycle and frequency.

2)   What is the relationship between duty cycle and frequency?

3)   What is the relationship between R1 and duty cycle?

4)   At what duty cycle does the SWO output have the least harmonic content? Why?

Experiment III Phase Locked Loop

Primary: _____   Assistant: _____

Signature: _____

Introductory Discussion:

This experiment will explore the operation of a phase locked loop (PLL). The primary components of such a device are the VCO and the phase comparator. These components will be studied separately through a variety of measurements.

Parts List:

IC1	1 – XR-2212 Phase Locked Loop
Ct	1 – 0.001 µF non-polarized Timing Capacitor
Ct	1 – 0.01 µF non-polarized Timing Capacitor
Cb	2 – 0.1 µF Bypass Capacitor
C1	1 – 250 pF Capacitor
Rt	1 – 10 kΩ Timing Resistor
Rt	1 – 30 kΩ Timing Resistor
R1	1 – 1 kΩ Resistor
R2	1 – 1 10 kΩ Resistor

Power Supply Specification:

Vcc   +10 V Positive Supply

Integrated Circuit Pin Description:

1	Vcc	Positive Supply
2	INP	Receive Analog Input
3	VCOOC	VCO Current Output
4	GND	Ground
5	VCOOV	VCO Voltage Source Output
6	COMP	Frequency Compensation Input (Uncommitted)
7	NINP	Inverted Input (Uncommitted)
8	OUT	Amplifier Output (Uncommitted)
9	PINP	Positive Input (Uncommitted)
10	PDETO	Phase Detector Output
11	Vref	Internal Voltage Reference
12	TIMR	Timing Resistor Input
13	TIMC2	Timing Capacitor Input
14	TIMC1	Timing Capacitor Input
15	VCOQO	VCO Quadrature Output
16	PDETI	Phase Detector Input

Functional Block Diagram:

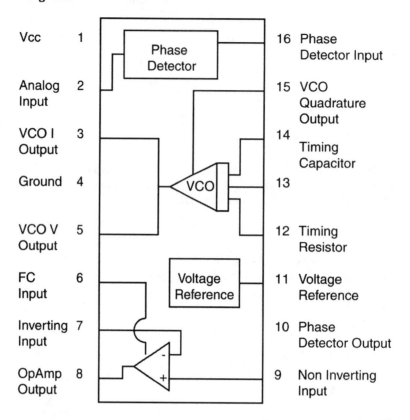

Figure III.1 – XR-2212 Block Diagram

Operational Overview:

The XR-2212 is composed of three primary functional blocks. The first is the VCO which has been explored previously and will be revisited now. The second is the phase detector which detects the phase difference between an applied signal and the VCO free running frequency. The third is the voltage reference which supplies a direct reading of the amount of phase difference between the applied signal and the VCO free running frequency.

Since frequency and phase are closely related mathematically, a phase difference can be associated with a frequency offset over a range of frequencies up to a maximum of +/− 50% of the free running frequency. There is one other component implemented, an uncommitted OPAMP, that will not be used.

Section 1:

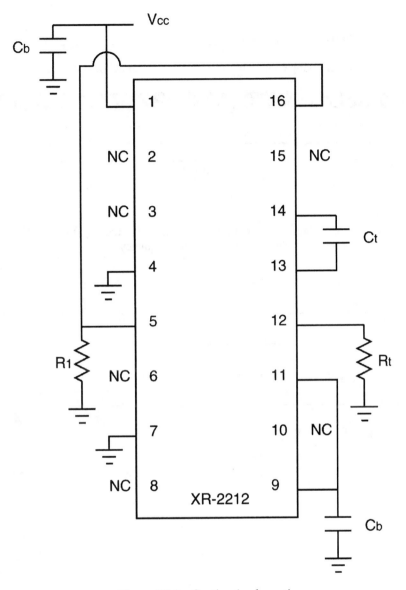

Figure III.2 – Section 1 schematic

Procedure:

1)   Connect the circuit as shown in Figure III.1. Use Ct = 0.001 μF and Rt = 10 kΩ.

2)   Calculate the VCO free running frequency using equation III-1.

$$f = \frac{1}{R_T C_T} \qquad \text{(III-1)}$$

Calculated free running frequency _____

17

3)   Measure this same frequency on pin 5.

        Measured free running frequency _____

4)   Using the following combinations of the timing capacitor and resistor, fill in table III.1.

Timing Resistor	Timing Capacitor	Measured Frequency
10 kΩ	0.001 µF	
10 kΩ	0.01 µF	
30 kΩ	0.001 µF	
30 kΩ	0.10 µF	

Table III.1

5)   Describe the relationship between the timing resistance and capacitance. Explain how
        these values change the VCO free running frequency.

_____

_____

_____

_____

_____

Section 2:

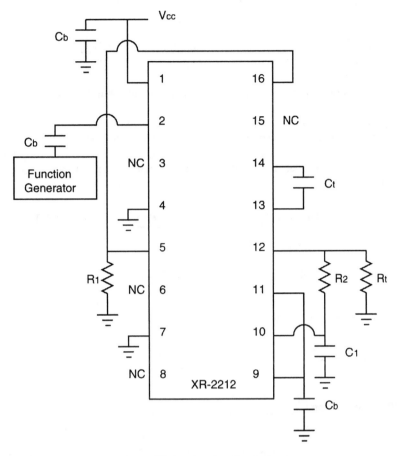

Figure III.3 – Section 2 schematic

Procedure:

1) Connect the circuit shown in Figure III.3. Adjust the Function generator for a sinusoidal output at 4 V p-p. Set the frequency to the VCO free running frequency measured in the previous section.

2) Monitor the Phase Detector Output, pin 10 on the oscilloscope. Slowly vary the frequency of the Function generator 10% and 20% below and above the VCO free running frequency. Describe the relationship between the quantities VCO free running frequency, input frequency, and Phase Detector Output Voltage. Enter the data in table III.2.

Function generator Frequency	Ftn. Gen Frequency Offset	Phase Detector Output
	+20%	
	+10%	
	VCO Free Running Frequency	
	−10%	
	−20%	

Table III.2

3) Repeat step 2 above, while monitoring the Internal Voltage Reference, pin 11. For what value of the Function generator does the voltage on this pin match the Phase Detector Output?

Pin 11 _____   Function generator Frequency _____

4) As the input frequency increases the Phase Detector Output Voltage _____?

5) While monitoring both the Function generator output frequency and the VCO Voltage Source Output, pin 5, vary the Function generator below and above the VCO free running frequency until the two signals lose lock. These two frequencies loop bandwidth of the PLL. Enter your data in the table below. Determine the lock range by applying equation III-2.

$$PLLLockRange = f_{upper} - f_{lower} \qquad\qquad \text{(III - 2)}$$

Lower lock limit _____

VCO free running frequency _____

Upper lock limit _____

PLL Lock Range _____

6) Experiment with the Function generator and the limits observed above, note how the PLL will maintain lock over the entire frequency range defined by the step above.

7) While still monitoring the same two signals, measure the phase difference between the Function generator input signal and the VCO Voltage Source Output. Vary the signal generator to the lock limits determined above and record your data in table III.4. If the PLL loses lock just enter "Lock Lost" for the phase difference.

Function generator Frequency Adjust	Function generator Output Frequency	Phase Difference
Upper Lock Limit		
+40%		
+30%		
+20%		
+10%		
VCO free running frequency		
−10 %		
−20%		
−30%		
−40%		
Lower Lock Limit		

Table III.3

8)   Now monitor the Phase Detector Output, pin 10, and adjust the Function generator to the same points as in step 7. Record the results in table III.4.

Function generator Frequency Adjust	Function generator Output Frequency	Phase Detector Output
Upper Lock Limit		
+40%		
+30%		
+20%		
+10%		
VCO free running frequency		
−10 %		
−20%		
−30%		
−40%		
Lower Lock Limit		

Table III.4

9)   Using Excel, plot your results from step 7 and 8 comparing the phase detector output and the phase difference.

Questions:

1)   Describe the operation of a VCO.

2)   Describe the operation of a phase comparator.

3)   Discuss how these two components combine to implement a PLL.

4)   Explain why a VCO used in a PLL application always has an inverse relationship between applied voltage (phase detector output) and frequency output (VCO voltage source output).

5)   Define lock range.

Experiment IV Harmonic Content Exploration

Primary: _____   Assistant: _____

Signature: _____

Introductory Discussion:

In this experiment, the use of a FFT module or Spectrum Analyzer will be used to analyze the harmonic content of three familiar waveforms. The frequency domain tool used will vary, this experiment is written for the HP 54600 series Digital Oscilloscope with an FFT plug-in. This experiment will also serve as an introduction to the use of a frequency domain instrument.

Parts List:

No parts needed.

Power Supply Specification:

N/A

Integrated Circuit Pin Description:

N/A

Functional Block Diagram:

N/A

Operational Overview:

Section 1:

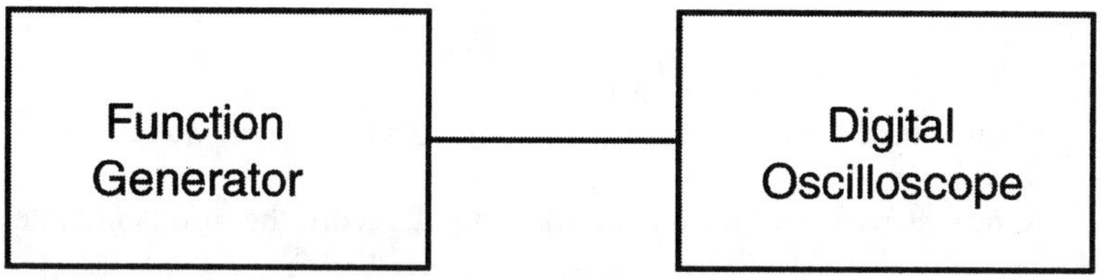

```
┌─────────────────┐          ┌─────────────────┐
│                 │          │                 │
│    Function     │──────────│    Digital      │
│   Generator     │          │  Oscilloscope   │
│                 │          │                 │
└─────────────────┘          └─────────────────┘
```

Figure IV.1 – Section 1 schematic

Procedure:

1)   Connect the instruments as shown in Figure IV.1. Be sure to apply the function generator to input 1 of the digital oscilloscope.

2)   Set the function generator as follows:

        Output Waveform: Sinusoidal
        Frequency: 1 MHz
        Voltage: 1 V p-p
        DC Offset: 0 V

3)   Observe the waveform using the oscilloscope and print out the signal.

4)   Change the display of your digital oscilloscope to the frequency domain. Set the frequency domain instrument as follows:

        Units/Division: 10 dB
        Reference Level: 10 dBV
        Center Frequency: 4 MHz
        Frequency Span: 8 MHz
        Window: Hanning

To set the digital oscilloscope in this mode perform the following steps. Make sure that the signal from the function generator is applied to input 1.

    1.   Press the +/– key.
    2.   Press Function 2 on.
    3.   Choose FFT mode.

5)   Record the amplitude and frequency for each component observed in table IV.1.

Component	Frequency	Measured Amplitude	Calculated Amplitude
Fundamental – 1 MHz			
2nd Harmonic – 2 MHz			
3rd Harmonic – 3 MHz			
4th Harmonic – 4 MHz			
5th Harmonic – 5 MHz			
6th Harmonic – 6 MHz			
7th Harmonic – 7 MHz			

Table IV.1

6)   Change the Function generator to a square wave output waveform.

7)   Repeat steps 3 – 6 for a square wave input, record the results in table IV.2.

Component	Frequency	Measured Amplitude	Calculated Amplitude
Fundamental – 1 MHz			
2nd Harmonic – 2 MHz			
3rd Harmonic – 3 MHz			
4th Harmonic – 4 MHz			
5th Harmonic – 5 MHz			
6th Harmonic – 6 MHz			
7th Harmonic – 7 MHz			

Table IV.2

8)   Change the function generator to a triangle wave output waveform.

9)   Repeat steps 3 – 6 for a triangle wave input, record the results in table IV.3.

Component	Frequency	Measured Amplitude	Calculated Amplitude
Fundamental – 1 MHz			
2nd Harmonic – 2 MHz			
3rd Harmonic – 3 MHz			
4th Harmonic – 4 MHz			
5th Harmonic – 5 MHz			
6th Harmonic – 6 MHz			
7th Harmonic – 7 MHz			

Table IV.3

Questions:

1)   Using Fourier series, compare the results obtained for each of the harmonic amplitudes to that which would be expected by calculation, enter the calculated values in each of the tables, IV.1 and IV.2 and IV.3. The formulas for each waveform are shown in equation IV-1, IV-2, and IV-3, respectively.

Note that the sinusoidal wave, in theory, has no harmonic energy; the square wave, again in theory, has harmonic energy only at the odd harmonics; and that the triangle wave has energy at all harmonics.

Experiment V Further Harmonic Analysis

Primary: _____   Assistant: _____

Signature: _____

Introductory Discussion:

In this experiment you will explore the effect of aliasing and the effect the number of samples and the choice of the windowing function on a FFT. Aliasing is the effect seen in an FFT when the sampling of the function is not at least twice as fast as the highest frequency component in the signal analyzed. While the precision of an FFT of a stable function is not increased by taking more samples, it is true that the choice of window used to limit the samples does have an effect.

The choice of window function involves a tradeoff between two effects; a loss of spectral resolution and an effect known as spectral leakage. Spectral resolution is a measure of how precisely the frequency can be measured. The greater the spectral resolution, the greater the accuracy of the frequency information on the FFT display. Spectral leakage is seen in the width of the frequency measured. The narrower this width, the greater the spectral leakage. Increased spectral leakage will also result in increased magnitude of adjacent frequency components.

In this experiment two window functions will be explored; Rectangular, and Hanning. These windows differ in how they limit the samples considered. The rectangular is a window N points wide with abrupt transitions on each end. Rectangular windows are used to discriminate between closely spaced frequency components. High spectral resolution is obtained at the cost of increased spectral leakage. The Hanning is similar in shape to the first cycle of a cosine wave; since it gradually rolls off at the edges, it does not provide the same spectral resolution or accuracy as the rectangular window. For most applications, the Hanning is a better choice as it provides a reasonable tradeoff between spectral resolution and leakage.

Parts List:

No parts needed.

Power Supply Specification:

N/A

Integrated Circuit Pin Description:

N/A

Functional Block Diagram:

N/A

Operational Overview:

Note that this experiment is written for the HP 54600 series Digital Oscilloscope with an FFT plug-in.

Section 1:

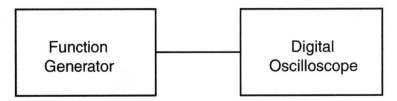

Figure V.1 – Section 1 schematic

Procedure:

1)   Connect the instruments as shown in Figure V.1. Make sure the signal is applied to input 1 of the digital oscilloscope.

2)   Set the function generator as follows:

Output Waveform:	Sinusoidal
Frequency:	10 kHz
Voltage:	2 V p-p
DC Offset:	0 V

3)   Set the frequency domain instrument as follows:

Units/Division:	10 dB
Reference Level:	5 dBV
Center Frequency:	10 kHz
Frequency Span:	~30 kHz
Window:	Hanning

4)   Measure the frequency and width of the frequency. Print out the result. Change the window function to Rectangular and repeat. Print out the result. Enter the values for frequency and width in table V.1.

Window Function	Frequency	Width
Hanning		
Rectangular		

Table V.1

5)   Change the center frequency to 50 kHz and the frequency span to 100 kHz. Print out the result for both windowing functions. Discuss the differences observed.

_____

_____

_____

_____

_____

Section 2:

In this section, aliasing will be demonstrated.

Procedure:

1) Set the function generator as follows:

   Output Waveform: Square Wave
   Frequency: 500 kHz
   Voltage: 2 V p-p
   DC Offset: 0 V

2) Set the frequency domain instrument as follows. To do this section, the frequency domain instrument must perform an FFT; analog spectrum analyzers cannot illustrate aliasing in this way.

   Effective Sampling Rate: 5 Msa/s
   Units/Division: 10 dB
   Reference Level: 10 dBV
   Center Frequency: 1.5 MHz
   Frequency Span: ~3 MHz
   Window: Hanning

3) Print out the result and note the amplitude of the fundamental, 3rd, and 5th harmonics. Record these in table V.2.

4) Change the Effective Sampling Rate to 500 ksa/s. Print out the result and note the amplitude of the fundamental, 3rd and 5th harmonics. Record these in table V.2. Also note that the spectrum does not appear the same. Examine closely between the fundamental and 3rd harmonics; there are new frequency components that were not present in the spectrum found in step 3. These are the result of aliasing and now appear at lower frequency components.

Sampling Rate	Fundamental	3rd Harmonic	5th Harmonic
5 Msa/s			
500 ksa/s			

Table V.2

Questions:

1) Why is prior knowledge of the input signal's bandwidth important when analyzing it using an FFT?

2) Is it still possible to obtain useful information from an FFT when aliasing has occurred? Why? What must you be careful about?

3) For broadband frequency measurements where relative frequency location is more important that precise frequency values, which window measurement is preferred?

Experiment VI AM DSB-LC Modulator

Primary: _____   Assistant: _____

Signature: _____

Introductory Discussion:

In this experiment you will explore the operation of an AM DSB-LC modulator using the XR-2206 IC as the modulator. The first section of the laboratory will determine the linear operating range of the modulator. The second and third sections will be used to explore the relationship between the amplitude and frequency of the modulated signal as a function of the modulating signal and modulation index.

Parts List:

IC1	1 – XR-2206 Function generator	
Ct	1 – 0.01 µF non-polarized Timing Capacitor	
Rt	1 – 20 kΩ Timing Resistor	
R1	2 – 5.1 kΩ Resistor	
R2	1 – 51 kΩ Resistor	
Cb	2 – 1 µF Bypass Capacitor	
C1	1 – 10 µF Capacitor	
R3	1 – 10 kΩ Variable Resistor (10-turn)	
R4	1 – 1 kΩ Variable Resistor (10-turn)	
R5	1 – 10 kΩ Pull up Resistor	

Power Supply Specification:

Vcc   + 12 V Positive Supply

Integrated Circuit Pin Description:

1	AMSI	Amplitude Modulating Signal Input
2	STO	Sine or Triangle Wave Output
3	MO	Multiplier Output
4	Vcc	Positive Supply
5	TC1	Timing Capacitor Input
6	TC2	Timing Capacitor Input
7	TR1	Timing Resistor Output
8	TR2	Timing Resistor Output
9	FSKI	Frequency Shift Keying Input
10	BIAS	Internal Voltage Reference
11	SYNCO	Sync. Output
12	GND	Ground
13	WAV1	Waveform Adjust Input 1 (THD)
14	WAV2	Waveform Adjust Input 2 (THD)
15	SYM1	Waveform Symmetry Adjust Input 1
16	SYM2	Waveform Symmetry Adjust Input 2

Functional Block Diagram:

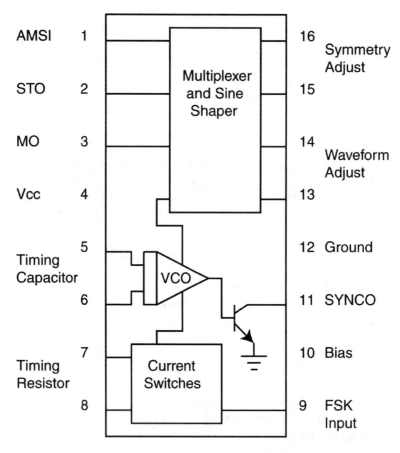

Figure VI.1 – XR-2206 Block Diagram

Operational Overview:

This integrated circuit is a function generator capable of generating sine, square wave, triangle, and ramp waveforms with variable harmonic content. Any of these output waveforms can be used as a carrier wave and amplitude modulated using the AMSI input. As will be seen in a later experiment these waveforms can also be frequency modulated. This device has many applications as a signal generator and will be used in later experiments as a signal source for investigation in pulse code modulation.

As can be seen from the block diagram this device is composed of three functional blocks. These are a VCO, an analog multiplexer and sine shaper, and a set of current switches. There is also a unity gain buffer amplifier connected to the primary output which serves to insulate the internal circuitry from connections made to that output. Note that the SYNCO output is an open collector output and hence requires an external pull up resistor for proper operation.

Section 1:

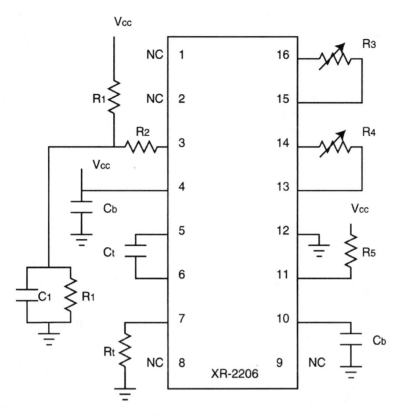

Figure VI.2 – Section 1 schematic

Procedure:

1) Connect the circuit shown in Figure VI.2.

2) Ground pin 1.

3) Connect pin 2 to an oscilloscope input and adjust R3 and R4 for the best waveform. Print out the resulting waveform. Show two complete cycles and adjust the amplitude for approximately full scale display.

4) Calculate the VCO free running frequency using equation VI-1 and enter on the line below.

$$f = \frac{1}{R_t C_t} \qquad (VI-1)$$

VCO free running frequency = _____

33

5) Connect a variable DC supply to pin 1. Vary the voltage from 0 V to 10 V in 1 volt steps. Measure the amplitude at pin 2 for each voltage and enter in table VI.1.

Applied Control Voltage	Output Amplitude
0 V	
1 V	
2 V	
3 V	
4 V	
5 V	
6 V	
7 V	
8 V	
9 V	
10 V	

Table VI.1

6) Plot your results using the Excel spreadsheet tool. On the horizontal axis show the control voltage, on the vertical axis show the output amplitude.

7) Over what range of control voltage is the output directly proportional to the applied control voltage?

_____

8) Over what range of control voltage is the output inversely proportional to the applied control voltage?

_____

9) At what exact control voltage did the output amplitude reach zero volts?

_____

Section 2:

Procedure:

1) Set the control voltage to the value determined in step 9 from section 1.

2) Connect pin 2 to an oscilloscope input. Adjust R3 and R4 for the best waveform.

3) Connect a function generator in series with the control voltage.

4) Set the function generator as follows:

Output Waveform:	Sinusoidal
Frequency:	1 kHz
Voltage:	4 V p-p
DC Offset:	0 V

5) Print out the waveform from pin 2. Adjust the time base so the display shows two complete cycles of the modulating waveform. (2 ms)

6) Adjust the output voltage of the function generator so the modulated signal observed on pin 2 is 100% modulated. (A modulation index of 1.) Record the peak voltage applied on the line below.

_____

7) Print out the waveform observed. Show two complete cycles of the modulated waveform.

8) Measure the maximum and minimum peak voltages of the modulated waveform. Enter your results on the lines below.

Vmax = _____   Vmin = _____

9) Calculate the peak voltage of the carrier signal using equation VI-2. Enter your result on the line below.

$$E_c = \frac{1}{2}\left[V_{max} + V_{min}\right] \qquad (VI - 2)$$

Ec = _____

$$E_m = \frac{1}{2}\left[V_{max} - V_{min}\right] \qquad (VI - 3)$$

10) Calculate the peak voltage of the modulating signal using equation VI-3. Enter your result on the line below.

Em = _____

11) Does your result agree with the peak voltage of the function generator? Why?

_____

_____

12) Calculate the modulation index using the experimentally determined values for the carrier voltage and modulating voltage. Use equation VI-4. Enter your result on the line below.

$$m = \frac{E_m}{E_c} \qquad (VI - 4)$$

m = _____

35

Section 3:

1) Using the experimentally determined value for carrier voltage, fill in table VI.2 for the values of modulation index shown.

Modulation Index	Peak Voltage of the Modulating Signal
0	
0.5	
1.5	
2.0	

Table VI.2

2) For each of the values in table VI.2 adjust the function generator to produce the appropriate modulating signal. On the oscilloscope show the modulating signal on input 1 and the modulated signal on input 2. Print out the display for each value of the modulation index. Show two cycles of the waveforms.

3) Set the function generator output for a modulation index of 1.0. Adjust the frequency of the function generator to each value shown below. Print out the display for each value of the modulating signal frequency. Show both waveforms as in the previous step.

Frequency 1:   500 Hz
Frequency 2:   1 kHz
Frequency 3:   2 kHz
Frequency 4:   5 kHz

Questions:

1) How is amplitude information carried in AM waveforms?

2) What is the distinguishing feature of an undermodulated AM waveform?

3) What is the distinguishing feature of an overmodulated AM waveform?

4) How is frequency information carried in AM waveforms?

5) What special relationship holds for the peak voltages of the modulating signal, carrier signal, and maximum voltage of the modulated waveform for 100% modulation? Express your answer in equation form.

Experiment VII AM Envelope Detector

Primary: _____   Assistant: _____

Signature: _____

Introductory Discussion:

In this experiment you will construct an envelope detector out of a single diode, capacitor, and resistor. This detector will be used to demodulate an amplitude modulated waveform that will be generated by the amplitude modulator constructed in Experiment VI.

Parts List:

IC1	1 – XR-2206 Function generator	
Ct	2 – 0.001 µF non-polarized Timing Capacitor	
Rt	1 – 20 kΩ Timing Resistor	
R1	3 – 5.1 kΩ Resistor	
R2	1 – 51 kΩ Resistor	
Cb	2 – 1 µF Bypass Capacitor	
C1	1 – 10 µF Capacitor	
R4	1 – 1 kΩ Variable Resistor (10-turn)	
R5	1 – 10 kΩ Pull up Resistor	
D1	1 – 1N914 Diode	
Rd1	1 – 10 kΩ Resistor	
Rd2	1 – 100 kΩ Resistor	
Cd	1 – 0.01 µF Capacitor	

Power Supply Specification:

Vcc   + 12 V Positive Supply

Integrated Circuit Pin Description:

1	AMSI	Amplitude Modulating Signal Input
2	STO	Sine or Triangle Wave Output
3	MO	Multiplier Output
4	Vcc	Positive Supply
5	TC1	Timing Capacitor Input
6	TC2	Timing Capacitor Input
7	TR1	Timing Resistor Output
8	TR2	Timing Resistor Output
9	FSKI	Frequency Shift Keying Input
10	BIAS	Internal Voltage Reference
11	SYNCO	Sync. Output
12	GND	Ground
13	WAV1	Waveform Adjust Input 1 (THD)
14	WAV2	Waveform Adjust Input 2 (THD)
15	SYM1	Waveform Symmetry Adjust Input 1
16	SYM2	Waveform Symmetry Adjust Input 2

Functional Block Diagram:

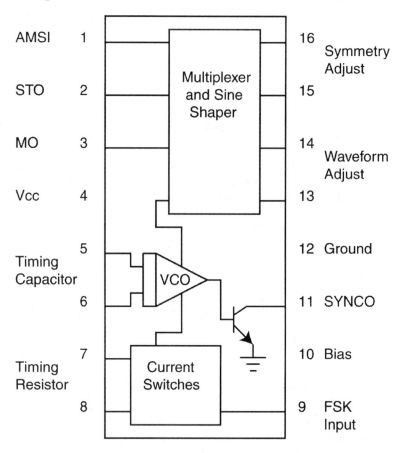

Figure VII.1 – XR-2206 Block Diagram

Operational Overview:

An envelope detector works because the diode turns on whenever it experiences a voltage difference across it equal to its threshold voltage. For a SI diode this is approximately 0.7 V. AM works by modulating the voltage of the carrier wave. As the carrier wave voltage grows above 0.7 V, the diode turns on and conducts. This places charge upon the capacitor equal to the peak voltage of the carrier minus the threshold voltage of the diode. As the carrier peaks and starts to return to its lower extreme, once it passes the threshold voltage the diode turns off and the capacitor discharges through the resistor.

This charging and discharging cycle effectively follows the amplitude modulated carrier wave, thereby generating a replica of the modulating signal minus the threshold voltage of the diode at the output. It is a replica of the modulating signal because the carrier modulation, and hence peak voltage, is directly proportional to the modulating signal. Proper selection of the detector resistor and capacitor yields optimum results.

Section 1:

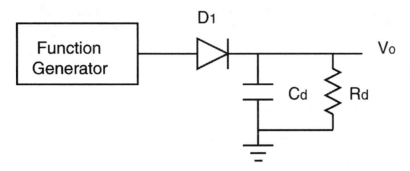

Figure VII.2 – Section 1 schematic

Procedure:

In this section, the performance of the envelope detector will be investigated using a function generator as the input.

1)   Before beginning the experimental procedure, the values of Cd and Rd will be calculated assuming a maximum modulating frequency of 2 kHz. While there is no modulation as yet on the carrier, the resistor and capacitor values will be determined assuming this is the maximum modulation rate. Refer to your text in Chapter 8 for the background of the equations.

2)   Verify that the Rd and Cd specified in the parts list match this calculation. Connect the circuit shown in Figure VII.2. If a polarized capacitor is used for Cd, connect the positive terminal to the output Vo.

3)   Set the function generator as follows:

Output Waveform:	Sinusoidal
Frequency:	1 kHz
Voltage:	4 V peak-to-peak
DC Offset:	0 V

4)   Connect input 1 of an oscilloscope to the function generator output. Connect input 2 of an oscilloscope to Vo. Set the time base so that several cycles of the input waveform are displayed. Print out the result.

5)   Change the function generator frequency to 100 kHz. Perform step 4 again.

6) Describe the difference between the two discharge cycles observed. In step 3 the frequency of the signal was low enough so that the entire discharge cycle could be observed. In step 5, this was not the case. Verify this to yourself using the two printouts, and discuss it on the lines below.

_____

_____

_____

_____

7) Vary the output amplitude of the function generator and describe the results you observe on the output waveform. Pay particular attention to that voltage where the output of the envelope detector goes to zero.

_____

_____

_____

8) Change the resistor value to 100 kΩ and restore the output amplitude of the function generator to 4 V peak-to-peak. Set the time base so that several cycles of the input waveform are displayed. Print out the result. Note that the difference between this result and that obtained in step 5 is the time constant is changed by a factor of 10. Which choice is the better one for minimizing ripple distortion? Why?

_____

_____

_____

_____

_____

9) Select which resistor you feel is the best choice, and reverse the diode and print out the waveforms from the oscilloscope. Describe your results. Would this circuit work as well as the earlier one? Why or why not?

_____

_____

_____

_____

_____

Section 2:

In this section, you will use the amplitude modulator constructed in Experiment VI as the input to the envelope demodulator. The only change is the addition of a high pass filter before the envelope detector. This is to block any DC component at the output of the amplitude modulator.

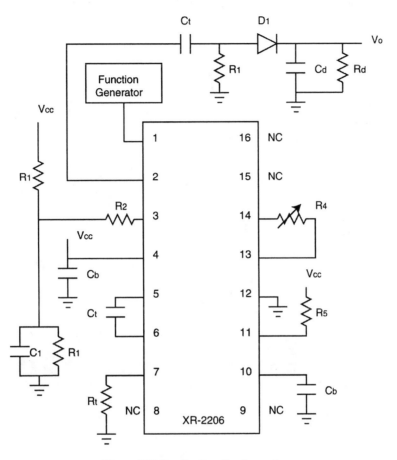

Figure VII.3 – Section 2 schematic

Procedure:

1) Connect the circuit shown in Figure VII.3. Set the function generator as follows:

Output Waveform: Sinusoidal
Frequency: 2 kHz
Voltage: 4 V peak-to-peak
DC Offset: 2 V

2) Lift the diode so that the envelope detector is not connected to the output of the modulator. Adjust the voltage and DC offset of the function generator for a modulation index of 1.0. Record the output voltage and DC offset below.

Output Voltage = _____

DC Offset = _____

Experiment VIII FM Modulator

Primary: _____   Assistant: _____

Signature: _____

Introductory Discussion:

In this experiment you will investigate two aspects of an FM modulator. These are frequency deviation, and the deviation sensitivity. This will be done in two sections, the first using the HP 33120 Function generator to simulate a FM signal. Then in section 2, we will use the XR-2206 to measure frequency deviation and measure deviation sensitivity.

Parts List:

IC1	1 – XR-2206 Function generator	
C1	1 – 10 µF Capacitor	
C2	2 – 0.001 µF Capacitor	
C3	1 – 0.01 µF Capacitor	
Cb	2 – 1 µF Bypass Capacitor	
R1	5 – 5.1 kΩ Resistor	
R2	1 – 51 kΩ Resistor	
R3	1 – 1 kΩ Variable Resistor (10-turn)	
R4	1 – 10 kΩ Resistor, 5%	
R5	1 – 5.1 kΩ Resistor, 5%	
R6	1 – 10 kΩ Variable Resistor (10-turn)	

Power Supply Specification:

Vcc   + 12 V Positive Supply

Integrated Circuit Pin Description:

1	AMSI	Amplitude Modulating Signal Input
2	STO	Sine or Triangle Wave Output
3	MO	Multiplier Output
4	Vcc	Positive Supply
5	TC1	Timing Capacitor Input
6	TC2	Timing Capacitor Input
7	TR1	Timing Resistor Output
8	TR2	Timing Resistor Output
9	FSKI	Frequency Shift Keying Input
10	BIAS	Internal Voltage Reference
11	SYNCO	Sync. Output
12	GND	Ground
13	WAV1	Waveform Adjust Input 1 (THD)
14	WAV2	Waveform Adjust Input 2 (THD)
15	SYM1	Waveform Symmetry Adjust Input 1
16	SYM2	Waveform Symmetry Adjust Input 2

Functional Block Diagram:

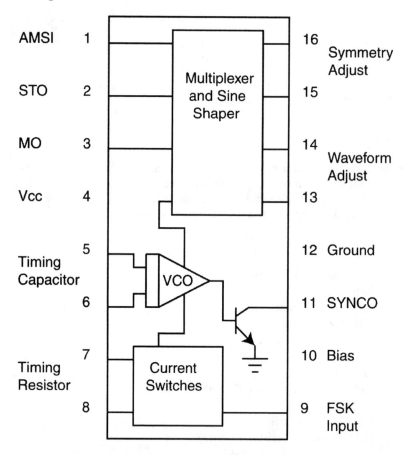

Figure VIII.1 – XR-2206 Block Diagram

Section 1:

Procedure:

1)   Connect the function generator to input 1 of the oscilloscope and set as follows:

Press SHIFT FM, select sinusoidal wave   To select FM modulation
Press FREQUENCY, set to 100 kHz   To select the carrier frequency
Press SHIFT FREQUENCY, set to 100 Hz   To select the modulation frequency
Press SHIFT LEVEL, set to 20 kHz   To select the frequency deviation

2)   The function generator is now operating as an FM modulator. Apply the function generator output to input 1 of the oscilloscope and the trigger output to input 2. Select input 2 to trigger the display on the oscilloscope. Adjust the timebase of the oscilloscope to illustrate between one and two cycles of the carrier. Select storage mode and print out the result.

44

3)   Change the frequency of the function generator to 1 Hz to observe the carrier frequency deviating. Calculate the two extreme periods you observe and record them below.

F1 Period Measured: _____   F1 Frequency Calculated: _____

F2 Period Measured: _____   F2 Frequency Calculated: _____

4)   What do you observe about the two frequencies? How are they related to the carrier frequency and the frequency deviation?

_____

_____

_____

5)   Restore the frequency to 100 Hz and change the frequency deviation to 1 kHz, 10 kHz, and 40 kHz and print out each result. Verify that the results agree with what you observed in step 4.

Section 2:

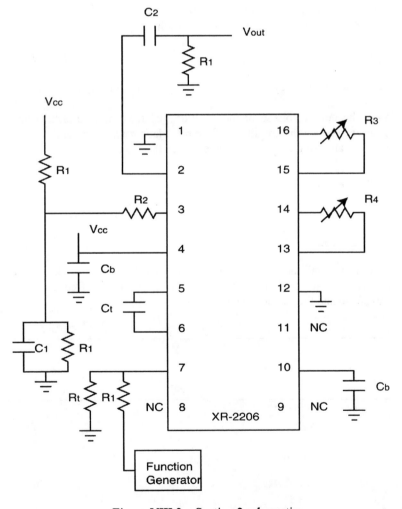

Figure VIII.2 – Section 2 schematic

45

Procedure:

1) Connect the circuit shown in Figure VIII.2. At this time, do not connect the function generator.

2) Measure the frequency at Vout and record. This is the carrier frequency.

F0 = _____

3) Connect the function generator and set as follows:

Output Waveform:	Sinusoidal
Frequency:	1 Hz
Voltage:	2 V p-p
DC Offset:	0 V

4) Connect Vout to input 1 of the oscilloscope, and the output of the function generator to input 2. Select input 2 as the trigger source. Adjust the display so that between 1 and 2 cycles of Vout are displayed. You should clearly see the carrier frequency deviating at 1 Hz.

5) Adjust the function generator to a frequency of 100 Hz. Record the two frequency extremes you observe and print out the results.

F1 Period Measured: _____ F1 Frequency Calculated: _____

F2 Period Measured: _____ F2 Frequency Calculated: _____

6) Vary the output voltage of the function generator and describe what relationship you observe between the amplitude of the modulating waveform and the frequency deviation. Here we are using the function generator as the modulating waveform.

_____

_____

_____

7) Return the amplitude to 2 V p-p and vary the frequency of the modulating waveform. Describe what relationship you observe between the frequency of the modulating waveform and the frequency deviation.

_____

_____

_____

8) Calculate the deviation sensitivity using the data collected and applying equation VIII-1. Note that Em is equal to 1 V as the equations developed in the text were for peak voltages.

$$K_2 = \frac{\Delta F}{\Delta V} = \frac{FD}{E_m} = \frac{|F_1 - F_2|}{1} \qquad \text{(VIII-1)}$$

$$K_2 = DeviationSensitivity$$

K2 = _____

9) Calculate the modulation index for this implementation using equation VIII-2.

$$m = \frac{FD}{w_m} = \frac{K_2 E_m}{2\pi f_m} = \frac{K_2(1)}{2\pi(100)} \qquad \text{(VIII-2)}$$

$$m = ModulationIndex$$

m = _____

Questions:

1) Discuss the concept of frequency deviation. Clearly indicate any proportional relationships you observed.

2) Discuss the relationship between the rate of frequency deviation and the frequency of the modulating signal.

3) Discuss the concept of deviation sensitivity.

4) Discuss how the concept of a modulation index as used here compares with that used in amplitude modulation. In particular discuss how both can be viewed as a "gain".

5) How are amplitude and frequency information in the modulating signal conveyed in an FM system?

Experiment IX FM Demodulator

Primary: _____   Assistant: _____

Signature: _____

Introductory Discussion:

In this experiment you will use the function generator to simulate an FM modulated signal and apply that to your demodulator. Following this verification you will use the circuit you built in Experiment VIII as a modulator to drive the demodulator you build using the 2212.

Parts List:

IC1	1 – XR-2212 Phase Locked Loop	
C1	3 – 0.001 µF non-polarized Timing Capacitor	
C2	1 – 30 pF Capacitor	
Cb	2 – 0.1 µF Bypass Capacitor	
R1	2 – 5.1 kΩ Resistor	
R2	2 – 100 kΩ Resistor	
R3	1 – 47 kΩ Resistor	
R4	1 – 10 kΩ Resistor	
R5	1 – 10 kΩ Variable Resistor	

Power Supply Specification:

Vcc   +10 V Positive Supply

Integrated Circuit Pin Description:

1	Vcc	Positive Supply
2	INP	Receive Analog Input
3	VCOOC	VCO Current Output
4	GND	Ground
5	VCOOV	VCO Voltage Source Output
6	COMP	Frequency Compensation Input (Uncommitted)
7	NINP	Inverted Input (Uncommitted)
8	OUT	Amplifier Output (Uncommitted)
9	PINP	Positive Input (Uncommitted)
10	PDETO	Phase Detector Output
11	Vref	Internal Voltage Reference
12	TIMR	Timing Resistor Input
13	TIMC2	Timing Capacitor Input
14	TIMC1	Timing Capacitor Input
15	VCOQO	VCO Quadrature Output
16	PDETI	Phase Detector Input

Functional Block Diagram:

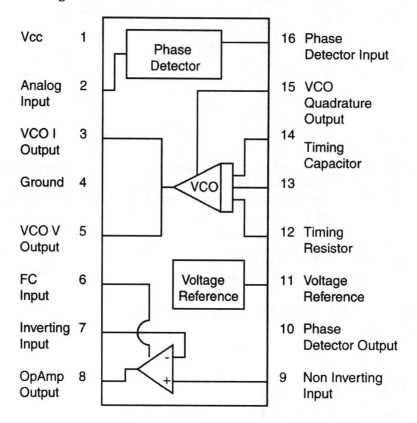

Figure IX.1 – XR-2212 Block Diagram

Section 1:

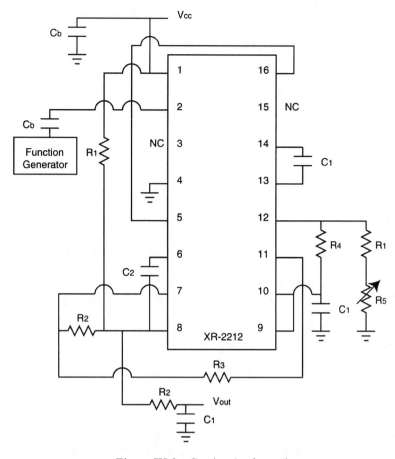

Figure IX.2 – Section 1 schematic

Procedure:

1)   Connect the circuit shown in Figure IX.2. Do not connect the Function generator at this time; instead, ground that node. Adjust R5 to approximately 5 kΩ.

2)   Disconnect R4 and adjust R5 to set the VCO free running frequency at 100 kHz. Monitor the frequency on pin 5. Once R5 has been set, reconnect R4.

3)   Connect the Function generator and set as follows:

Press SHIFT FM, select sinusoidal wave   To select FM modulation
Press FREQUENCY, set to 100 kHz   To select the carrier frequency
Press SHIFT FREQUENCY, set to 100 Hz   To select the modulation frequency
Press SHIFT LEVEL, set to 20 kHz   To select the frequency deviation

4)   The Function generator is now operating as a FM modulator. Apply the Function generator output to input 1 of the oscilloscope, and Vout to input 2 of the oscilloscope. Print out the result.

5)   Change the Function generator modulation frequency to 20 Hz. Print out the result.

6)   Describe the results you observed in steps 4 and 5. The first modulation frequency is the upper end of the audiophile range, 20 kHz, the second the lower end, 20 Hz. How did the modulated signal change at these two settings?

_____

_____

_____

_____

Section 2:

1)   Remove the function generator from the schematic in section 1.

2)   Take the circuit you constructed in Experiment VIII and apply the function generator to the input of the XR-2206 on pin 7.

3)   Apply the output of the XR-2206 to where the function generator was attached in Figure IX.2.

4)   Set the function generator as follows:

Output Waveform: Sinusoidal
Frequency: 1 kHz
Voltage: 1 V p-p
DC Offset: 0 V

5)   Connect the function generator output to input 1 of the oscilloscope and Vout to input 2 of the oscilloscope. Adjust the time base so that two cycles of the function generator output are shown. Print out the result. Compare the two waveforms, are there any differences?

_____

_____

_____

_____

6)   Vary the function generator output frequency and amplitude. Discuss your observations below. Specifically state how the output signal of the demodulator changes in proportion to any changes in the modulating signal generated by the function generator.

_____

_____

_____

_____

_____

Questions:

1) What is the relationship between the FM modulating signal and the demodulator output?

2) How does the PLL act to aid the process of FM demodulation? Recall that a PLL can be viewed as a frequency to voltage translator. Why is this function important to FM demodulation?

Experiment X PCM CODEC/COMBO

Primary: _____   Assistant: _____

Signature: _____

Introductory Discussion:

This experiment will introduce you to the operation of a commercially important CODEC. This device converts analog voice signals into PCM encoded DS-1 frame formatted digital signals suitable for use in the telephone system. You will examine how this device works with one simulated voice input. The telephone system will be simulated by a strap connecting the PCM output to the PCM input.

Parts List:

IC1	1 – TP3054 CODEC COMBO
Cb	2 – 0.1 µF Bypass Capacitor
R1	2 – 10 kΩ Resistor
Ra	1 – 1 kΩ
Rb	1 – 400 Ω
C1	1 – .1 µF
IC2	1 – 555 Timer

Power Supply Specification:

Vcc	+ 5 V Positive Supply
Vee	– 5 V Negative Supply

Integrated Circuit Pin Description:

1	Vee	Negative Supply
2	GND	Ground
3	VfrO	Analog Output
4	Vcc	Positive Supply
5	FSr	Receive Frame Sync. Pulse
6	Dr	Receive PCM Data Input
7	BCLKr	Bit Clock
8	MCLKr	Receive Master Clock
9	MCLKx	Transmit Master Clock
10	BCLKx	Output Shift Bit Clock
11	Dx	Transmit PCM Data Output
12	FSx	Transmit Frame Sync. Pulse
13	TS	Encoder Time Slot Pulse
14	GSx	Gain Select Transmit Amplifier
15	VFxI-	Inverting Input Transmit Amplifier
16	VFxI+	Noninverting Input Transmit Amplifier

Functional Block Diagram:

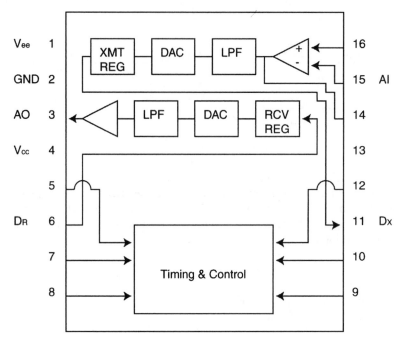

Figure X.1 – TP-3054 Block Diagram

Operational Overview Discussion:

The TP-3054 is composed of several functional blocks as illustrated above. However, as can be seen there are two primary data paths that are of interest, transmit and receive. On the transmit side, a buffer amplifier to allow externally set gain is followed by a filter element to ensure the signal reaching the sample and hold DAC is bandlimited below 4 kHz. After the comparator, not shown, is used to set the polarity bit the PCM word is sent to the transmit register.

On the receive side, the same operations occur only in reverse sequence. The other main functional area is the large timing and control block where the internal timing signals are derived from the externally applied ones.

In examining the signal on pin 6, the thing to remember is that this chip is intended to operate in a commercial telephone environment. Here, there are many simultaneous conversations going on all the time. With a 1.544 MHz master clock, and 8 kHz frame clock, this chip is designed to work with a TDM system routing in DS-1 frames.

Since this experiment does not use the full capability of outputting an 8 bit PCM word for each of 24 channels in a DS-1 frame, the output will consist of a single group of 8 bits, every 8 kHz. Then a space for the other 23 channels, the framing bit, then another single group of 8 bits. Thus the signal seen at pin 6 is a quick burst of a single PCM word, followed by a long period of no data, followed again by a quick burst of a single PCM word.

Section 1:

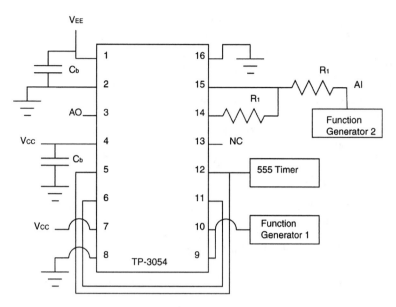

Figure X.2 – Schematic

Proceedure:

1)   Connect the circuit shown in Figure X.2.

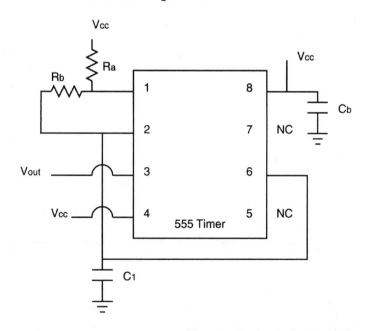

Figure X.3 – 555 Timer Schematic

2)   Connect the 555 Timer circuit shown in Figure X.3 and apply the AI input as shown in Figure X.2. Verify that the 555 Timer circuit is generating an 8 kHz signal.

3)   Set function generator 1 as follows:

Output Waveform: Square Wave
Frequency: 1.544 MHz
Voltage: Adjust to TTL   Enter Value used: _____
DC Offset: Adjust to TTL   Enter Value used: _____

4)   Set function generator 2 as follows, and apply to AI:

Output Waveform: Sinusoidal
Frequency: 1 kHz
Voltage: 2 V p-p
DC Offset: 0 V

5)   Verify that the signal seen on pin 14 is similar to signal applied from function generator 3. Print out the signal.

6)   Verify presence of signal at pin 6. Print out the signal.

7)   Verify that the signal on pin 3 is similar to signal applied from function generator 2. Print out the signal.

8)   In the above steps you have traced the signal through the IC. Now place one probe on pin 15 and another probe on pin 3. Adjust the oscilloscope to display both signals. Note the phase difference seen. Print out the signal. Record it below.

Phase Difference Measured _____

Section 2:

1)   Connect your oscilloscope probe to pin 6 or pin 11. Examine the signal observed. You should see a series of "spikes". Measure the time between each of these "spikes". Convert this to a frequency and record both your measurement and calculation below.

Time _____   Frequency _____

2)   What significance do these measurements have? Review your text on the frame time exhibited by a standard DS-1 PCM frame as used in the telephone system. Answer in the space provided below.

_____

_____

_____

_____

3)   Using an oscilloscope with a delayed sweep function, zoom in on one of the "spikes". Print out the results. Record the logical values seen in table X.2.

4)   Scroll the scope to the next eight "spikes" observed. Record these in table X.2 as well.

58

5)   Observe that each of these represents a single PCM code word of 8 bits. Using table X.1 convert each of these measurements to a numeric value corresponding to the output voltage. Then find the input voltage they correspond to by applying equation X-1. This will require algebraic manipulation of equation X-1 to solve for Vi with your measured Vo values. Note that the first bit is the sign bit. Note that μ=255. Remember that the voltage readings are peak voltages. Enter these calculations in Table X.2.

Input Voltage Value, Vi	TP 3054 Encoding Format, μ-Law
+ Full Scale	10000000
+ 0	11111111
− 0	01111111
− Full Scale	00000000

Table X.1

$$|V_0| = \frac{\ln[1 + \mu|V_i|]}{\ln[1 + \mu]} \qquad 0 \le |V_i| \le 1 \qquad (X\text{-}1)$$

Measured code word	Numeric value, Vo	Input voltage, Vi

Table X.2

6)   Graph your results from table X.2. Show the Vi voltages as a series of PAM samples and connect the peaks of these voltages. Determine the period and probable shape of the graphed waveform. Is it what you expect? Why?

Questions:

1)   Describe any differences seen between the signal on pin 14 and that seen on pin 3.

2)   In step 4 you measured a phase difference; does this make any difference? Ask yourself the question, have you ever heard a phase error when talking on the telephone?

Note that this is not like the echo that is sometimes heard. You should understand that voice signals, and analog signals in general, are very insensitive to phase shifts. On the other hand, digital signals are not. Therefore, the phase shift observed makes no difference.

3)   What is the significance of the period between the "spikes" seen on pin 6 or pin 11?

4)   What determines if the area between the spikes is high or low? Hint: Examine the last bit of the code word immediately preceding the area.

Experiment XI Huffman Codes

Primary: _____   Assistant: _____

Signature: _____

Introductory Discussion:

Huffman codes make use of the probabilities of the various symbols being sent. As in the Morse code, it is desirable to have the most frequently used symbols to have the shortest encoding. Huffman codes are classified as variable length source codes.

To build a Huffman code is straightforward. A set of symbols, along with the probabilities that they occur is provided. It is then a process of reduction and splitting to find the Huffman code. Huffman codes are not unique. It is possible to end up with different codes depending on the initial choices of assignments. However, all Huffman codes for the same alphabet are the same average lengths. That is, if you multiply the probability of each symbol times its length and add them up the total is the same for any Huffman code generated.

For the following alphabets, form Huffman codes. Show all work including groupings. Begin the splitting process by assigning a 0 to the highest probability code, and reorder the codes so the highest probability is listed first. Since this experiment would be very easy to copy, the following pledge is required from the primary. Please sign below.

On my honor, I swear that all work is my own.   Your Name: _____

Symbol	Probability	1st Reduce	2nd Reduce	3rd Reduce
S1	0.4			
S2	0.2			
S3	0.2			
S4	0.1			
S5	0.1			

Table X1.1 Reduction table 1

Symbol	3rd Code	3rd %	2nd Code	2nd %	1st Code	1st %	Choice	%
S1		0.4					0	
S2		0.2					1	
S3		0.2						
S4		0.1						
S5		0,1						

Table X1.2 Split table 1

Find the average length of the code generated. Show your calculation on the line below.

_____

Symbol	Probability	1st Reduce	2nd Reduce	3rd Reduce	4th Reduce	5th Reduce
S1	0.3					
S2	0.2					
S3	0.15					
S4	0.15					
S5	0.1					
S6	0.05					
S7	0.05					

Table X1.3 Reduction table 2

Symbol	5th Code	5th %	4th Code	4th %	3rd Code	3rd %	2nd Code	2nd %	1st Code	1st %	Choice	%
S1		0.3									0	
S2		0.2									1	
S3		0.15										
S4		0.15										
S5		0.1										
S6		0.05										
S7		0.05										

Table X1.4 Split table 2a

Now do the split for alphabet 2 again, this time with different initial choices.

Symbol	5th Code	5th %	4th Code	4th %	3rd Code	3rd %	2nd Code	2nd %	1st Code	1st %	Choice	%
S1		0.3									1	
S2		0.2									0	
S3		0.15										
S4		0.15										
S5		0.1										
S6		0.05										
S7		0.05										

Table X1.5 Split table 2b

Find the average length of the two codes generated on the previous page. Show your calculations on the lines below.

2a: _____

2b: _____

Questions:

1)   Discuss your results for the average length of the two codes done in part 2.

2)   Discuss how the initial choice of a code bit for the split process impacts average length. Are the two codes generated in part 2 equally good?

Experiment XII Code Trees

Primary: _____   Assistant: _____

Signature: _____

Introductory Discussion:

Code trees are an interesting way to build variable length source codes. A code tree approach, unlike the Huffman approach, results in codes that always have unique prefixes.

Additionally, unlike the Huffman approach, codes developed using the code tree approach can result in very different average lengths, depending on the probabilities the alphabet exhibits and the initial choices made assigning the codes. An important part of using a code tree to develop a code is to ensure the shortest average length code results.

For each of the following alphabets, develop the shortest average length code possible. Since this experiment would be very easy to copy, the following pledge is required from the primary. Please sign below.

On my honor, I swear that all work is my own.   Your Name: _____

Symbol	Probability
S1	0.30
S2	0.30
S3	0.15
S4	0.15
S5	0.10

Table XII.1 Alphabet 1

Show the code tree below:

Find the average length of the code generated. Show your calculation on the line below.

Symbol	Probability
A	7
B	2
C	2
D	4
E	8
F	2
G	4
H	2
I	7
J	2
K	4
L	2
M	7
N	7
O	4
P	2
Q	2
R	4
S	4
T	8
U	4
V	2
W	4
X	2
Y	2
Z	2

Table X11.2 Alphabet 2

Note that this assignment of percentages to the English alphabet is only for demonstration purposes and is not scientifically determined. To a rough approximation, it follows the Morse code variable length assignment. There are 2 symbols @ 8%, 4 symbols @ 7%, 8 symbols @ 4%, and 12 symbols @ 2%.

Show the code tree below:

Find the average length of the code generated. Show your calculation on the lines below.

_____

_____

_____

_____

Experiment XIII BFSK Modulator

Primary: _____   Assistant: _____

Signature: _____

Introductory Discussion:

This experiment will investigate BFSK. BFSK is a simple and inexpensive form of FSK. The unmodulated carrier frequency, in an analogy to FM, is deviated to the mark and space frequencies. A Function generator is used to simulate the modulated signal and this generator is applied to pin 9. Recalling how the XR-2206 worked in Experiment I, the function generator is acting like a switch, selecting one of two frequencies set by the resistors attached to the binary keying inputs.

Parts List:

IC1	1 – XR-2206 Function generator
C1	1 – 10 µF Capacitor
C2	1 – 0.001 µF Capacitor
C3	1 – 0.01 µF Capacitor
Cb	2 – 1 µF Bypass Capacitor
R1	3 – 5.1 kΩ Resistor
R2	1 – 51 kΩ Resistor
R3	1 – 1 kΩ Variable Resistor (10-turn)
R4	1 – 10 kΩ Resistor, 5%
R5	1 – 5.1 kΩ Resistor, 5%
R6	1 – 10 kΩ Variable Resistor (10-turn)

Power Supply Specification:

Vcc   + 12 V Positive Supply

Integrated Circuit Pin Description:

1	AMSI	Amplitude Modulating Signal Input
2	STO	Sine or Triangle Wave Output
3	MO	Multiplier Output
4	Vcc	Positive Supply
5	TC1	Timing Capacitor Input
6	TC2	Timing Capacitor Input
7	TR1	Timing Resistor Output
8	TR2	Timing Resistor Output
9	FSKI	Frequency Shift Keying Input
10	BIAS	Internal Voltage Reference
11	SYNCO	Sync. Output
12	GND	Ground
13	WAV1	Waveform Adjust Input 1 (THD)
14	WAV2	Waveform Adjust Input 2 (THD)
15	SYM1	Waveform Symmetry Adjust Input 1
16	SYM2	Waveform Symmetry Adjust Input 2

Functional Block Diagram:

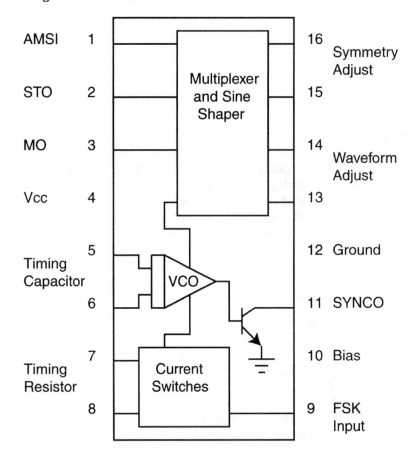

Figure XIII.1 – XR-2206 Block Diagram

Operational Overview:

This operational overview of this integrated circuit can be found in Experiment V. In this experiment the value of the timing resistors will be used to set the signaling frequencies, mark and space for investigation into BFSK. A function generator will be applied to the FSK input to simulate the modulating signal, and the BFSK modulated signal output will be taken from pin 2, STO.

Section 1:

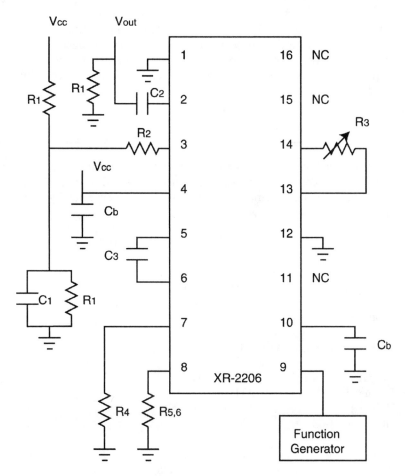

Figure XIII.2 – Section 1 schematic

Procedure:

1)   Connect the circuit shown in Figure XIII.2. Use the R5 resistor. Do not connect the function generator at this time; instead, ground pin 9.

2)   Connect the oscilloscope to Vout and adjust R3 for a minimum distortion sinusoid.

3)   Record the frequency measured at Vout. This is the unmodulated carrier frequency.

F = _____

4)   Connect the function generator to pin 9. Set the function generator as follows:

Output Waveform: Square Wave
Frequency: 1 mHz
Voltage: 2 V peak-to-peak
DC Offset: 0 V

71

5)   Using the oscilloscope connected to Vout, measure the two frequencies seen. The lower of these two frequencies is the mark frequency and the higher is the space frequency. Recall that the mark frequency corresponds to a logical 1, and the space frequency corresponds to a logical 0. In this step, the function generator is acting as a modulating signal, +1 V a logical 1, -1 V a logical 0. The low frequency of the signal generator should allow you to make the measurement of the two frequencies easily. If there is difficulty, stop the sweep and measure each waveform individually. Print out each waveform.

Fmark = _____   Fspace = _____

6)   The two signaling frequencies are determined by the values of the resistors connected to pins 7 and 8, coupled with the capacitance connected to pins 5 and 6. Calculate the signaling frequencies, mark and space, that would be expected by using equations XIII-1 and enter on the lines below.

$$ f_{mark} = \frac{1}{R_4 C_3} \qquad\qquad f_{space} = \frac{1}{R_5 C_3} \qquad\qquad \text{(XIII-1)} $$

Fmark = _____   Fspace = _____

7)   Set the function generator as follows:

Output Waveform: Square Wave
Frequency: 2 kHz
Voltage: 2 V peak-to-peak
DC Offset: 0 V

8)   Connect Vout to input 1 and pin 9 to input 2 of the oscilloscope. Adjust the time base such that between 2 and 3 periods of the Function generator output are displayed. Verify that the higher frequency corresponds to that of a logical 0 and the lower frequency to that of a logical 1. Print out the result.

9)   Disconnect pin 9 from the oscilloscope and either attach Vout to a spectrum analyzer or use the FFT module to display the BFSK spectrum. (Refer to Experiment IV for how to put the HP 54600 into FFT mode.) Adjust the frequency domain instrument as follows:

Units/Division: 10 dB
Reference Level: 5 dBV
Center Frequency: 15 kHz
Frequency Span: ~30 kHz
Window: Hanning

10)   Print out the resulting spectrum. Note how the two spectra around each signaling frequency interact. Specifically, note the harmonics each has, how the harmonics fall off as one moves away from the signaling frequency, and how the harmonics add to produce non-symmetrical spectra around each signaling frequency.

11)   Calculate the minimum signaling bandwidth that is required using the Nyquist criterion. Apply equation XIII-2.

$$BW = 2f_m + f_{space} - f_{mark} \qquad (XIII - 2)$$

BW = _____

12)   Compare the calculation with the bandwidth seen in step 10. Why does there exist significant spectral energy, harmonic energy, outside the calculated bandwidth? Hint: Think about the harmonic content of the modulating waveform, here simulated by the function generator. Recall that all the modulation process does is shift the harmonic content of the modulating waveform to some new frequency because BFSK can be seen as the sum of two DSB-SC modulated waveforms centered at the signaling frequencies.

_____

_____

_____

_____

_____

13)   Calculate the minimum bandwidth possible for BFSK using equation XIII-3.

$$MinimumBWBFSK = 4f_m \qquad (XIII - 3)$$

Minimum BW BFSK = _____

14)   Assuming that the mark frequency does not change, calculate the start and stop frequencies expected for a minimum BW BFSK waveform.

Start Frequency = _____   Stop Frequency = _____

15)   Calculate the signaling frequency and resistor value for R6 that would result in the minimum bandwidth calculated in step 13.   Recall that the combination of R6 and C3 determine the space frequency and the mark frequency is held constant.

Fspace = _____   R6 = _____

16)   Exchange R5 for the variable resistor R6. Monitoring the spectral output of Vout, adjust R6 for the condition calculated above, minimum bandwidth. Print out the resulting spectrum, leaving the frequency span at 30 kHz. Vary R6 and observe the results on the output spectrum. Make sure to not let the value of R6 fall below 1 kΩ!

Questions:

1) Describe the basic concept of BFSK.

2) What is the relationship between the logical value of the modulating signal and the signaling frequencies in the modulated signal?

3) What is the relationship between the frequency of the modulating signal and the signaling frequencies in the modulated signal? Specifically, do the signaling frequencies change if the modulating signal frequency changes?

Experiment XIV BFSK Demodulator

Primary: _____   Assistant: _____

Signature: _____

Introductory Discussion:

In this experiment you will investigate BFSK demodulation. In the first part, the HP 33120 Function generator is used to generate a BFSK signal and the demodulation circuitry is verified. Additionally, using the function generator you will experiment with frequency deviation and determine how the spectrum bandwidth is affected. In the second part, the circuit built in the previous experiment is used to generate the BFSK modulated signal.

Parts List:

IC1	1 – XR-2212 Phase Locked Loop
C1	3 – 0.001 µF non-polarized Timing Capacitor
C2	1 – 30 pF Capacitor
Cb	2 – 0.1 µF Bypass Capacitor
R1	2 – 5.1 kΩ Resistor
R2	2 – 100 kΩ Resistor
R3	1 – 47 kΩ Resistor
R4	1 – 10 kΩ Resistor
R5	1 – 10 kΩ Variable Resistor

Power Supply Specification:

Vcc	+10 V Positive Supply

Integrated Circuit Pin Description:

1	Vcc	Positive Supply
2	INP	Receive Analog Input
3	VCOOC	VCO Current Output
4	GND	Ground
5	VCOOV	VCO Voltage Source Output
6	COMP	Frequency Compensation Input (Uncommitted)
7	NINP	Inverted Input (Uncommitted)
8	OUT	Amplifier Output (Uncommitted)
9	PINP	Positive Input (Uncommitted)
10	PDETO	Phase Detector Output
11	Vref	Internal Voltage Reference
12	TIMR	Timing Resistor Input
13	TIMC2	Timing Capacitor Input
14	TIMC1	Timing Capacitor Input
15	VCOQO	VCO Quadrature Output
16	PDETI	Phase Detector Input

Functional Block Diagram:

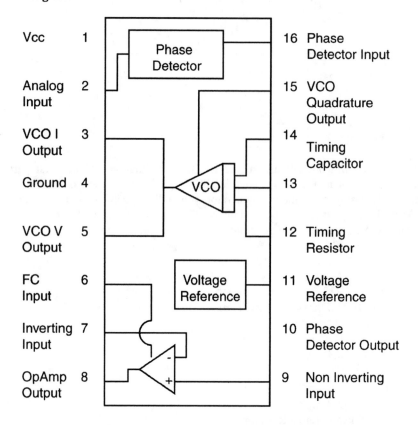

Figure XIV.1 – XR-2212 Block Diagram

Section 1:

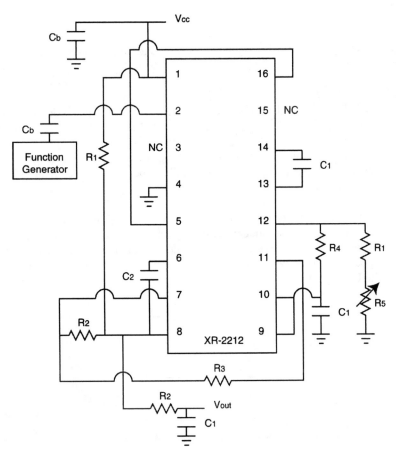

Figure XIV.2 – Section 1 schematic

Procedure:

1) Connect the circuit shown in Figure XIV.2. Do not connect the function generator at this time; instead, ground that node. Adjust R5 to approximately 5 kΩ.

2) Disconnect R4 and adjust R5 to set the VCO free running frequency at 100 kHz. Monitor the frequency on pin 5. Once R5 has been set, reconnect R4.

3) Connect the function generator and set as follows:

Output Waveform: Sinusoidal
Frequency: 80 kHz
Voltage: 2 V peak-to-peak
DC Offset: 0 V

4) Measure the DC voltage at Vout.

Vout = _____

5) Change the function generator to oscillate at 120 kHz, and measure Vout.

Vout = _____

6) Cycle the power on the function generator and set as follows:

Press SHIFT FM, select square wave   To select BFSK modulation
Press FREQUENCY, set to 100 kHz   To select the carrier frequency
Press SHIFT FREQUENCY, set to 100 Hz To select the modulation frequency
Press SHIFT LEVEL, set to 40 kHz   To select the frequency deviation

7) The function generator is now operating as a BFSK modulator. Apply the function generator output to input 1 of the oscilloscope, and Vout to input 2 of the oscilloscope. Print out the result.

8) Experiment with the function generator by varying the frequency deviation. What effect does varying the frequency deviation have on the output of the function generator? Make sure you observe and report both the time domain and frequency domain results. Specifically state what you observe about the signaling frequencies and the bandwidth of the FSK spectrum.

_____

_____

_____

_____

_____

_____

9) What effect does varying the frequency deviation have on the output of the demodulator? Monitor Vout while varying the frequency deviation and record your results below.

_____

_____

_____

_____

Section 2:

1) Remove the function generator from the schematic in section 1.

2) Take the circuit you constructed in Experiment XIII and apply the function generator to the input of the XR-2206 on pin 9.

3) Apply the output of the XR-2206 to where the Function generator was attached in Figure XIV.1.

4)	Set the function generator as follows:

	Output Waveform:		Square Wave
	Frequency:			100 Hz
	Voltage:			1 V peak-to-peak
	DC Offset:			0 V

5)	Record the peak-to-peak voltage seen on Vout.	Print out the result from the oscilloscope.

	Vout = _____

6)	Connect the function generator output to input 1 of the oscilloscope, and Vout to input 2 of the oscilloscope. Vary the function generator in both amplitude and frequency and discuss your observations below. Print out results for modulation frequencies of 1 kHz, 2 kHz, 3 kHz, 4 kHz, and 5 kHz. On each printout show two cycles of the waveforms.

	_____

	_____

	_____

	_____

	_____

	_____

7)	Congratulations, you have now constructed your first modem!

Questions:

1)	The relationship between the BFSK modulating signal frequency and the demodulator output frequency.

2)	The relationship between the BFSK modulating signal amplitude and the demodulator output amplitude. Specifically, discuss why the two signals are not the same amplitude and what this says about communication systems.

3)	What limited the maximum frequency of the modem observed in step 6? Specifically, discuss how the rise and fall times of the demodulator output waveform have an impact on this. What determines the rise and fall times of the output waveform? Is it affected by the modulating signal's frequency? Why?

Experiment XV Pulse Width Modulation

Primary: _____   Assistant: _____

Signature: _____

Introductory Discussion:

This experiment will use the 555 Timer circuit to build a pulse width modulator (PWM). The technique that is used is to modulate the control voltage pin, thereby modulating the internal threshold voltage. This produces a PWM circuit.

The IC pin description assumes a single 555 Timer packaged into an 8 pin DIP. Other packages are available. Check the implementation you are using and if necessary change the schematic to reflect the pin assignments.

Parts List:

IC1	1 – 555 Timer
Ra	1 – 3 kΩ Resistor
Rb	1 – 500 Ω Resistor
C1	1 – 0.01 µF Capacitor
Cb	1 – 0.01 µF Bypass Capacitor

Power Supply Specification:

Vcc   +5 V Positive Supply

Integrated Circuit Pin Description:

1	Ground
2	Trigger
3	Output
4	Reset
5	Control Voltage
6	Trigger
7	Discharge
8	Vcc

Section 1:

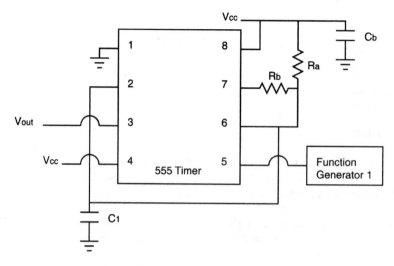

Figure XV.1 – Section 1 PWM Schematic

Procedure:

1)   Connect the circuit shown in Figure XV.1. Function generator 1 acts as the modulation input. Set function generator 1 as follows:

Output Waveform:	Sinusoidal
Frequency:	1 kHz
Voltage:	2 V peak-to-peak
DC Offset:	4 V

2)   Connect the output from the circuit just constructed to input 1 of the oscilloscope. Connect the output from function generator 1 to input 2 of the oscilloscope. Adjust the time base of the oscilloscope to display two complete cycles of the modulating signal and print out. Adjust the time base of the oscilloscope to display a few representative areas of the PWM output and print these out as well.

3)   Examine the display carefully and describe the results you see. Specifically, what effect does the modulating voltage have on the modulated signal?

_____

_____

_____

_____

_____

_____

_____

_____

4) Vary the modulating signal peak-to-peak amplitude. Describe the results you observe on the modulated signal as a result of these changes.

_____

_____

_____

_____

_____

_____

5) Vary the shape of the modulating signal try a square wave and a triangle wave. Describe the results you observe on the modulated signal as a result of these changes.

_____

_____

_____

_____

_____

_____

6) Vary the modulating signal peak-to-peak amplitude. Describe the results you observe on the modulated signal as a result of these changes.

_____

_____

_____

_____

_____

_____

Questions:

1) Summarize the technique of PWM. Specifically address how the modulated waveform changes as a function of the modulating waveform.

Experiment XVI CRC Codes

Primary: _____   Assistant: _____

Signature: _____

Introductory Discussion:

In this experiment you will design and "construct" using Electronics Workbench a CRC-4 polynomial divider. To get you started on this a similar design using the same tools will be shown building a CRC-5 divider. The two polynomials are equations XVI-1 and XVI-2.

$$CRC - 4 : x^4 + x + 1 \qquad (XVI-1)$$

$$CRC - 5 : x^5 + x^4 + x^2 + 1 \quad (XVI-2)$$

The first step is to render the polynomial divider into circuit block diagram form. For the CRC-5 polynomial this is shown in figure XVI.1.

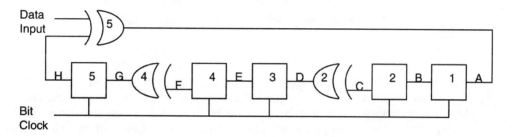

Figure XVI.1 – CRC-5 Block Diagram

This figure shows that for this polynomial three XOR gates and five D-FFs are required to implement it. The D-FFs are the blocks where the D input is to the right and the Q output to the left. The clock input is from below. Note that where the coefficient of the polynomial is non-zero, both an XOR gate and a D-FF exist. Where the coefficient is zero, just the D-FF exists. This rule is followed for all cases except when the power of x is zero, (e.g. when it is equal to 1). In that particular case, neither the D-FF nor the XOR gate exists.

Further, note that the feedback paths are at the locations where the polynomial has non-zero coefficients, and that the feedback occurs just after the placement of the associated D-FF. In the figure above, the letters A – H are used so that you can check the waveforms you obtain against the key presented below for the CRC-5 design. This will give you confidence that your solution for the CRC-4 problem is correct. Figure XVI.2 shows the waveforms along with the bit clock and input data sequence. Recall that the input data sequence is generated by the transmitted data word shifted by the power of the polynomial.

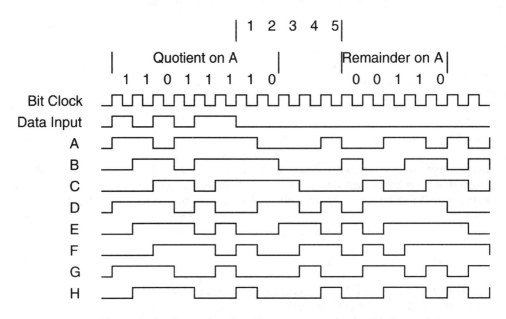

| 1 2 3 4 5 |

| Quotient on A | Remainder on A |
| 1 1 0 1 1 1 1 0 | 0 0 1 1 0 |

Bit Clock

Data Input

A

B

C

D

E

F

G

H

Remainder is on A, after 5 zeros are clocked into register

Both quotient and remainder are output MSB to LSB

Figure XVI.2 – CRC-5 waveforms

As can be seen by examining figure XVI.2, the data input is 10101100. The quotient, (result) of the division is clocked out on output A. The remainder of the division is clocked out of the output A after the register is cleared by clocking in five zeros. This is because the order of the polynomial is five, so five zeros must be clocked in to clear the register. Once this is done the next five bits output on A are the remainder. Note that the remainder is clocked out MSB to LSB, just as the data input was clocked in.

The file used for this demonstration is available from the instructor. It uses the word generator supplied with Electronics Workbench to generate the data input sequence and the logic analyzer to display the results at each output. While it is possible to proceed directly to solving the laboratory without examining the demonstration file, please take a few minutes to look it over and feel free.

To document your results print out the schematic, logic analyzer, word generator, and parts list. The version of Electronics Workbench on your system may not allow printout of the logic analyzer, this printout is necessary to document your results. If this is the case, try the following: with the logic analyzer open, press ALT PrintScrn and open Paint from the Accessories menu of Windows. Then from the Edit pulldown menu select Paste, and print out the result. This will allow documentation of your results.

Finally, use the data input sequence used in the appendix of your text for this problem. That will provide another location for you to check your results. That data sequence is 11011010.

Questions:

1)   What problems did you run into in constructing this circuit? Would the shift register work as well if you reversed the direction of the input? Why or why not?

Experiment XVII COMNET III Introduction

Primary: _____   Assistant: _____

Signature: _____

Introductory Discussion:

This experiment will introduce you to the CACI COMNET III simulation engine. This is a powerful tool for simulating LAN and WAN networks. It features a drag and drop interface for quick and easy generation of the network that is to be simulated. The simulator contains two basic building blocks that are used to construct the network topology:

      1)   nodes
      2)   links

Nodes are of three types; processor, router and switch. A good example of a processor node would be a computer workstation. A processor node can simulate the running of software, generation of packets, and storage on an internal disk from which files may be read and written to. A single processor node icon can be used to represent any number of identical computers by configuring it as a group node.

A router node is used to simulate joining devices such as routers, bridges, switches, and hubs. A router node can do anything a processor node can as well as simulate the function of the joining device. Any router node has some significant elapsed time, latency, between when a message appears on an input and when it appears on an output. This is the main difference between a router node and a switch node. Switch nodes do not simulate the latency common to many types of joining devices.

Links are used to model different media and link layers. A link icon has the properties of bandwidth and propagation delay, and the unit of exchange is at layer 2, the frame. A frame has the attributes of size, overhead, and error rate. Many different link layer protocols are simulated along with the physical media.

Once the network topology has been constructed, the message traffic on that network must be modeled. COMNET III does this by using a flexible scheduling tool that allows you to schedule the traffic originating from any node or groups of nodes as well as any responses that you specify.

In this first experiment using this tool you will build a simple 4-node Ethernet 10BaseT network with e-mail traffic between two nodes.

Procedure:

The first thing to do is start up the simulation engine. Do this by going to the start menu and selecting COMNET III. The simulation engine will load and you will see a blank screen. Next, select and place the computers that will be the e-mail sources. These are modeled as processor nodes. To select and place them on the screen choose the third icon down on the RHS that looks like a box. Click on the icon and move the mouse over the screen; you should see an outline. Just click where you want to place the node. Go ahead and place four of them on the screen. You will note that COMNET III automatically names these nodes for you, e.g.: Node1, Node2, and so forth.

87

The next thing to do is to configure each node's properties. To do this, right click on the first node placed, Node1, and select the **Properties...** item. You will see a dialog box labeled Node Properties. The node type and parameters are shown. Since for this first laboratory we will be using the default properties, for now cycle through the tabs and options to get familiar with them and then select the Icon menu in the upper left hand corner. Since we are using this node to simulate a computer workstation, choose the computer icon on the menu. Click OK and the icon should change. Do the same thing for the other three nodes.

The next thing to do is to connect the nodes just placed. To do this select the link icon representing a CSMA/CD link. This is the eighth icon down on the RHS. It looks like a horizontal bar with two nodes above and two below the line. Click on the icon and drag it to the screen. Place it approximately in the center of the four nodes. Next, the nodes must be connected to the link. This is done in COMNET through the use of arcs. There are two types of arcs that can be used, diagonal and horizontal/vertical. They are the second icons on the RHS and LHS respectively. Choose whichever you prefer and click on it. To connect each node to the link, just click once on a node icon and once on the link. A line or arc will appear connecting the two icons. Note that you must click on the arc icon after each link is completed. Connect all four nodes to the link icon.

This is a good time to save your network. To do so, choose the File menu and select Save as... Click on the new folder icon and create a folder on your hard drive called EET_465. Double click to open the folder and save the file as Experiment17. Note that the title bar of COMNET III now shows the file name Experiment17.

The next thing to do is to set the properties of the link node. To do this right click on the node icon and select **Properties...** The Type field confirms that we have selected the right icon; it shows CSMA/CD. The Parameters field is set to DEFAULT. To change this click once on the little box with the two dots on it that lies just to the right of the Parameters field. This brings up a parameter listing of all types of CSMA/CD networks in the library. Choose the 802.3 CSMA/CD 10BASET library selection by clicking once on it. The Copy>> bar should then light up. Click once on it and the library selection will move to the parameters list. Click Done and if it has not already appeared, choose the library selection just made on the Parameters menu. Finally, change the name of the link icon to 802.3 CSMA/CD 10BASET. Click OK on the Link Properties dialog box and the new name should appear.

The next thing to do is to define message sources and responses to simulate the e-mail traffic. This will be done by placing message icons and connecting them to the appropriate node. Select the message source icon; it is the ninth icon on the LHS and it looks like a sheet of paper with an arrow pointing to the right. Click once and place it near Node1; it should default to the name Msg6. Connect Msg6 to Node1 by using an arc. The line that connects them should be a different color than the lines connecting the nodes to the link. That is because it is representing a software program inside the node, not a physical link from a node to a joining device represented here by a link icon.

To configure the properties of the message source right click on it and select **Properties...** First, change the name of the message source to e-mail source. For this experiment the scheduling of the e-mail messages will be by iteration, this means that every iteration time an e-mail message will be sourced from this node. To set the time, select the Scheduling tab, set the Interarrival time to Exp(10.0), and click on the box with the two dots on it that lies immediately to the right. This brings up another dialog box where the mean time of the distribution can be set. For this experiment set it to 5.0. Click OK to close the dialog box. You have now set the source interarrival time to an exponential distribution with a mean time of 5.0 seconds. This means that in an exponential distribution about a mean time of 5.0 seconds a message will be sourced from this node.

The next item to set is the message size and how that will vary. Since e-mail messages vary in size, so will our model. Select the **Messages** tab and set Msg size calc to Probability distribution. Change the Prob distrib field to 900.0 and make sure the Msg size units is set to Bytes. This sets the average message size to 900 bytes. Next, we will set the destination of the e-mail messages we are simulating. To do this select the **Destinations** tab and set Destination type to Random neighbor. This means that the destination of each e-mail message is a random selection of the other nodes connected to the link. Next, select the **Text** tab to define the content of the e-mail message. You will choose the text of the e-mail message. To do this set Msg text option to Set message text and enter a short message in the message text box.

The last item to be set is found by selecting the **Packets** tab. Here, you can set the application type that is generating the message. Since this application is an e-mail message, click the small box with two dots immediately to the right of the field Application type. Click Add... and type e-mail in the Name field displayed. Click OK, click Done. The Application type field should now read e-mail. Click OK and you should return to the layout of your network with the e-mail source connected to Node1.

Again, this is a good time to save your progress so go ahead and do it remembering that since you have already named the file all that is needed is to click Save from the File pulldown menu. The next several steps generate an e-mail response program and place it on Node2. This program will generate the responses to the e-mail messages that Node1 is generating.

Select the Response source icon, the ninth icon on the RHS that looks like a letter with an arrow curving in and out of it. Place it near Node2 and connect it with an arc. Open the properties of this icon by right clicking on it and choosing **Properties...** First, change the name of this icon to e-mail responder. Click on the **Edit Received Messages...** box and remove any items in the Received Message List. Now click **Add...** and examine the list of received message text that appear. Your message should be on the list; use the down arrow to select your message, and click OK and Done.

Just like the situation in sourcing the messages, the simulation engine must be told how to simulate the responses to the e-mail messages; this is done by selecting the Messages tab. Note that this is exactly like the Messages dialog box that was used in the source message icon. This time we will select a different probability distribution, a geometric response. Click the down arrow next to Prob distrib and select Geo(0.0,1.0). To modify this default distribution click on the little box with the two dots next to it. As can be seen this is a geometric distribution of about 1.0 with a standard deviation of 1.41. That tells us that the message size is 1 byte long with the standard deviation noted. This is much too short. Set the mean length of the message to 2000 and the minimum message size to 200. The next tab is **Destinations**. Make sure the ECHO item is checked. This will send the response back to the source, just like a response to an e-mail. Select the tab **Text** and change the Msg text option to Set message text, then type in a message text to respond to your original message. Select the tab **Packets** and choose Application type e-mail.

This completes the definition of the response message source. We now need to specify what statistics we wish to see on our output. Do this by clicking on the Report pulldown menu. Choose the Select Reports... item and click on it. We will choose to include reports from the Nodes, Links, and Message and Response Sources menus. Double click on the Nodes item. Double click on the Received Message Counts item. Select ALL and ON and click OK. Double click on the Links item. Double click on the Channel Utilization item. Select ALL and ON and click OK. Double click on the Collision Stats item. Select ALL and ON and click OK. Double click on the Message and Response Sources item. Double click on the Message Delivered item. Click ALL and ON and click OK. Click Done.

To demonstrate the power of the simulation engine to calculate and display graphs, we will specify one plot. To do this go to the e-mail responder response source icon and right click to get statistics. Click on this item. This will display a statistics requests dialog box. Double click on

Real-Time Message Delay. Set the initial X axis minimum to 60 and click the On box. Click OK and Done. This will generate this plot after the simulation is run.

Now you will verify your model will run. To do this click on the pulldown menu Simulate and click on Verify Model. If you have done everything correctly a message "No verification error detected." will appear in the lower right hand corner of the screen. Next, you need to set the parameters for the simulation. click on the pull down menu Simulate and click on Run Parameters... Here you will set the length of the simulation. Set the Warmup length to 20 seconds and the Replication length to 120 seconds. Leave the number of replications at 1, click OK. Next, set the animation on; to do this click on the pull down menu Simulate and click on Animate.... check Animate packet flow, and click OK.

You are now ready to simulate your network. To do so, save it once more and on the Simulate pulldown menu select Start Simulation. You may want to refer to the GIF image from the simulator placed at the end of the experiment to verify your work. This shows an image of the desktop for this simulation file.

As you run the simulation a window should appear labeled RTTracePlot – e-mail responder Delay from Node 2. This is a response time plot of the time in seconds that Node 2 took to respond to the e-mail message that was specified earlier. Note that while the plot starts at 0 time, the curves seen do not begin until 25 seconds of simulation time have passed. This is because we have set the Warmup length to 20 seconds in our simulation. As can be seen the mean response time stays fairly flat over the length of the simulation. This plot can be printed just by clicking on the printer icon on the toolbar of the plot window, although for most laser printers all you will see is a big black rectangle due to the dark background of the plot area.

The next item to investigate is the reports that were selected earlier. To do this click on the pulldown menu Report and click on Browse Reports. Inside the file folder for this experiment you will find a file titled Stat1.rpt. Note that this is the default name for the report file. If you run the simulation again, this report file will be overwritten.

To open this file just click on it and select Open. This will open up the application Notepad and display the file in that application. If you want to save this report, now is a good time to rename it and Save as in the Notepad pulldown menu File.

On the top line of the report you will find the date and time of the run along with the title of the experiment. Below that is a line indicating what report was requested, here received message counts, along with the simulation run time. As you can see this first report is quite straightforward with four lines, Node 1 showing 13 messages from Node 2 and Nodes 2 through 4 showing the number of messages from Node 1. Note that in this simulation Node 4 did not see all the messages from Node 2. This is due to the fact that the simulation has a fixed cutoff time and the engine did not have enough time to simulate this. In actual fact all stations on a LAN such as that simulated here see all messages from every node.

Page 2 of the report shows the channel utilization of the 10BaseT network. 58 frames were delivered with 0 received in error. The average transmission delay was ¾ of a second and the standard deviation and maximum delivery times are also listed. The last column shows what percentage utilization of the network this traffic consumed. As you can see the number here is very small.

The third page lists collision statistics for the network. Since the utilization was so small and only two nodes were exchanging information, one would not expect any collisions and none were observed. Page 4 gives more detailed information on the messages and responses from each node. This includes messages assembled and statistics on delay time of message delivery.

This report can be printed out by selecting Print from the File pulldown menu of the Notepad application. Before printing, make sure to select Page Setup and set the page style to Landscape. This will yield a much nicer printout. Even with this selection you will find the print out of the report to contain a large amount of white space but you will avoid the line wrap problem that is seen if the printout is done in Portrait mode.

Questions:

1) Why does the number of messages reported in the receive message count not match the number of frames listed in the channel utilization report? (Hint: Does each message necessarily fit into just one frame? Check the message size specified and the maximum frame size allowed by this LAN Data Link layer.)

2) Expand on why you would not expect to see any collisions on this LAN. If the simulation was run to infinite time, could one or more collisions be expected? Why? (Hint: Recall that CSMA/CD is a not a deterministic bandwidth allocater; instead, it is a shout first and listen later.)

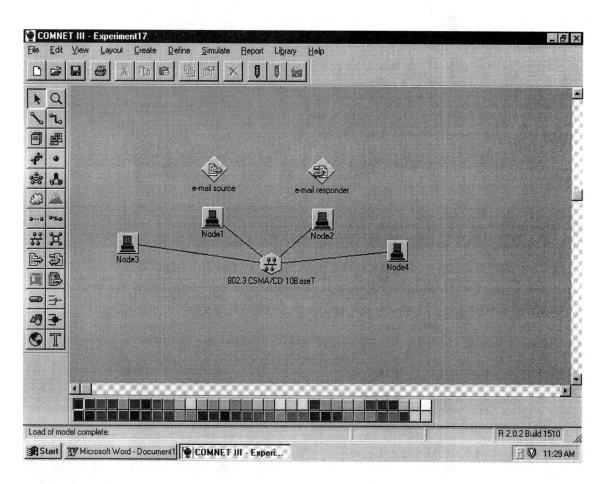

Stat1.rpt

CACI COMNET III Release 2.0.2 Build 1510 Mon May 24 07:32:01 1999 PAGE 1

Experiment17

NODES: RECEIVED MESSAGE COUNTS

REPLICATION 1 FROM 20.0 TO 140.0 SECONDS

RECEIVER	COUNT	MESSAGE NAME
Node1	13	e-mail response msg
Node2	13	e-mail source msg
Node3	13	e-mail source msg
Node4	10	e-mail source msg

CACI COMNET III Release 2.0.2 Build 1510 Mon May 24 07:32:01 1999 PAGE 2

Experiment17

LINKS: CHANNEL UTILIZATION

REPLICATION 1 FROM 20.0 TO 140.0 SECONDS

LINK	FRAMES DELIVERED	RST/ERR	TRANSMISSION DELAY (MS) AVERAGE	STD DEV	MAXIMUM	% UTIL
802.3 CSMA/CD 10BaseT	58	0	0.839	0.233	1.230	0.0404

Experiment17

LINKS: COLLISION STATS

REPLICATION 1 FROM 20.0 TO 140.0 SECONDS

LINK NAME   802.3
                             CSMA/CD
                             10BaseT

ACCESS PROTOCOL   CSMA/CD

COLLISION EPISODES   0

COLLIDED FRAMES   0

NBR OF TRIES TO RESOLVE
     AVERAGE   0.00
     STANDARD DEVIATION   0.00
     MAXIMUM   0

NBR OF DEFERRALS   0

DEFERRAL DELAY (MS)
     AVERAGE   0.00
     STANDARD DEVIATION   0.00
     MAXIMUM   0.00

Stat1.rpt

DEFERRAL QUEUE SIZE (FRAMES)
AVERAGE   0.00
STANDARD DEVIATION   0.00
MAXIMUM   0

MULTIPLE COLLISION EPISODES
NBR EPISODES   0
AVG PER EPISODE   0.00
MAX PER EPISODE   0

Experiment17

MESSAGE + RESPONSE SOURCES: MESSAGE DELIVERED

REPLICATION 1 FROM 20.0 TO 140.0 SECONDS

ORIGIN / MSG SRC NAME: DESTINATION LIST	MESSAGES ASSEMBLED	MESSAGE DELAY AVERAGE	STD DEV	MAXIMUM
Node1 / src e-mail source:				
Node3	13	0.744 MS	0.000 MS	0.744 MS
Node2	13	0.744 MS	0.000 MS	0.744 MS
Node4	10	0.744 MS	0.000 MS	0.744 MS
Node2 / src e-mail responder:				
ECHO	13	1.681 MS	1.204 MS	4.502 MS

Experiment XVIII COMNET III LAN/WAN

Primary: _____   Assistant: _____

Signature: _____

Introductory Discussion:

This experiment will take the LAN simulated in Experiment XVII and expand on it by adding a WAN link between two LANs and exchanging messages both on the LAN and across the WAN. The WAN link will be a T-1 line between two 10BaseT LANs.

Procedure:

This file is already prepared for you in the folder labeled Experiment 18. Additionally, the desktop image from the simulator can be found at the end of the experiment. The paragraphs below walk you through the procedure to generate it. This should be helpful in familiarizing you with the simulator.

The first thing to do is start up the simulator and load Experiment 17. Use the mouse to select all items on the screen by "drawing" a box around them and selecting Copy from the Edit pulldown menu. Then select Paste and position the outline square where you choose. This will replicate a second LAN identical to the first on the screen. Note that the nodes and links are renamed for you. Now save the file as Experiment 18 in a new folder of the same name.

The next thing is to add the WAN link. To do this select the seventh icon on the LHS. It looks like two small spheres connected with a lightning bolt. This is the point to point WAN icon. Place it on the screen. Now, since one cannot connect a WAN link directly to a LAN, we will need to add two network devices to terminate the WAN link. Place two of these on the screen using the network device icon, the fourth icon on the LHS. Then connect these using the diagonal arc icon, the second icon on the LHS.

To set the properties of the WAN link, right click and select properties... On the Link Type tab, choose a Point-To-Point type and click the .. box to the right of the parameters line. From the library selections on the right, choose T1 (DS1) and click Copy>>. Click Done, click OK. Next set the network device properties. These will be configured as Cisco 2500 routers. Perform the same steps as done immediately above to set these device types.

Next, we must set up an e-mail session across the WAN link. To do this add a new e-mail source to Node 3 and a new e-mail responder to Node 10. Do this in the same way as in the previous experiment. Set the source to send to a random list but the responder to just the originator node. The easiest way to do this is to copy, paste, and modify the original e-mail source and responders. Here, the names and messages were changed slightly to clearly indicate what messages come across the WAN and those that are local to the LAN.

The next item is to include all the new nodes and link we have defined in the report list. Select the Report pulldown menu and for each of the four reports selected in the last experiment, modify them to include all items. e.g. select ALL ON. Further, to allow you to see the animation, go to each responder, left click and select statistics. Turn all graphs OFF.

Verify the model and run. Since we have not added new items to any of reports we will get reports similar to the last experiment, but with more nodes and links specified.

The first summary, received message counts, shows a total of 85 messages. These are broken down into four groups. Note the importance of identifying the message source or destination by a unique message. Note also that it must fit into the limited space provided for in the report! If you did not make a unique set of messages or chose messages too long, this report will be of limited use. Go back and use unique short messages for each e-mail source or responder.

You should see a received message total, really frame total, such as the following:

Receiver Node	Message Count	Source Node
1	9	3
2	6	3
2	7	1
3	8	1
4	11	1
4	9	3
9	7	8
10	7	8
11	6	8
16	5	3
16	5	1
17	5	8

Note that all the messages received were from one of the three nodes that were designated as e-mail sources. This is just what you should expect. The number of messages received by each node is determined by the statistics of how the random neighbor is selected. If you choose you can specify specific destinations for some e-mail sources and change the statistics.

Turning to the next table, link channel utilization, we see that of the 85 frames delivered, 60 were on the original LAN and 25 were on the second LAN, called link12. Again, the third table showing collision statistics demonstrates that we are still not stressing the CSMA/CD protocol on the LAN at all. The fourth table gives more detail on the messages received by each node, essentially expanding the first table.

However, something looks wrong. There are no messages from the e-mail responders and no link utilization over the WAN! How can we fix this? There are three things that must be done.

First, right click on each of the responder message sources and select properties. Select the scheduling tab and click on edit received messages. Highlight and delete the message that consists of more than 1*. This will ensure that the message sent from the responder will use the message text we specified and will be identifiable in the report summary.

The second item lies in how we specified the destination list for the messages. We used random neighbor. It turns out that the simulation engine uses this to indicate only those nodes reachable in one hop from the origin as neighbors. Since we are using a WAN link and there are two routers on it, this is defined as a two hop length. To fix this, use random list and specify the nodes you want the messges to be sent to. Make sure you specify those nodes that are designated as responders, 2, 9, and 10. Probably the easiest thing to do is just choose all nodes for the destination list. This is what is done in this file.

The last thing to do is to lengthen the time of the simulation since we have so many more nodes. Change the run parameters to a time of 220 seconds. This will double the simulation time and give us a better picture of what is happening in this network architecture. Now run the simulation and print out the report.

Questions:

1) Analyze the report in terms of the message counts seen at each node. Reconcile the number of source messages and response messages in terms of communication across the two LAN networks. Be sure to include the following items:

A) The number of messages received at each node specifying from which node it was sent.

B) The type of message received at each node, e.g. was it a message that was responded to or just seen on the LAN as it passed by?

C) The number of messages received by each router and the three link types. Do these totals reconcile with what you would expect from your earlier analysis of this data? Why? Give specific examples.

D) Discuss in general why again no collisions are seen on either LAN. Would you expect there ever to be any on the WAN if the simulation was extended into infinite time? Why?

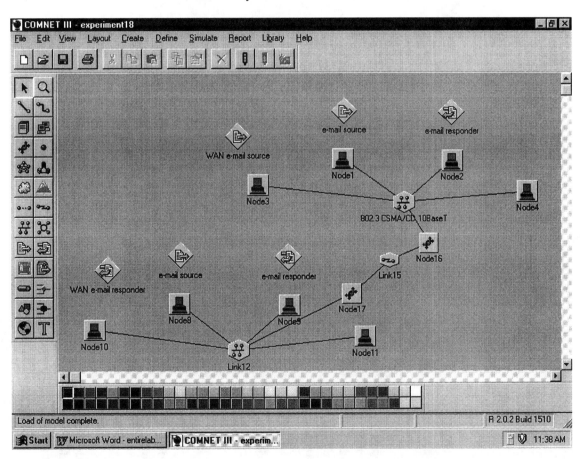

Stat1.rpt

CACI COMNET III Release 2.0.2 Build 1510 Mon May 24 09:02:06 1999 PAGE 1

experiment18

NODES: RECEIVED MESSAGE COUNTS

REPLICATION 1 FROM 20.0 TO 240.0 SECONDS

RECEIVER	COUNT	MESSAGE NAME
Node1	5	e-mail response msg 2
Node1	8	e-mail source msg 2
Node1	3	WAN e-mail source msg
Node1	10	e-mail response msg 1
Node1	5	WAN e-mail response msg
Node1	5	e-mail source msg 1
Node2	6	WAN e-mail source msg
Node2	10	e-mail source msg 1
Node2	4	e-mail source msg 2
Node3	3	e-mail source msg 1
Node3	6	e-mail response msg 1
Node3	5	WAN e-mai response msg
Node3	3	e-mail response msg 2
Node3	6	e-mail source msg 2
Node3	4	WAN e-mail source msg
Node4	5	e-mail source msg 1
Node4	9	WAN e-mail source msg
Node4	4	e-mail source msg 2

98

experiment18

NODES: RECEIVED MESSAGE COUNTS

REPLICATION 1 FROM 20.0 TO 240.0 SECONDS

RECEIVER	COUNT	MESSAGE NAME
Node8	4	e-mail response msg 2
Node8	5	e-mail source msg 2
Node8	8	WAN e-mail source msg
Node8	6	e-mail source msg 1
Node8	4	e-mail response msg 1
Node9	5	e-mail source msg 1
Node9	4	e-mail source msg 2
Node9	3	WAN e-mail source msg
Node10	5	WAN e-mail source msg
Node10	5	e-mail source msg 1
Node11	6	e-mail source msg 2
Node11	4	WAN e-mail source msg
Node11	1	e-mail source msg 1
Node16	6	e-mail source msg 1
Node16	6	e-mail source msg 2
Node16	5	WAN e-mail source msg
Node17	6	WAN e-mail source msg
Node17	3	e-mail source msg 2
Node17	5	e-mail source msg 1

experiment18

LINKS: CHANNEL UTILIZATION

REPLICATION 1 FROM 20.0 TO 240.0 SECONDS

LINK	FRAMES		TRANSMISSION DELAY (MS)			% UTIL
	DELIVERED	RST/ERR	AVERAGE	STD DEV	MAXIMUM	
802.3 CSMA/CD 10BaseT						
Link12	179	0	0.777	0.246	1.230	0.0630
Link15	121	0	0.791	0.234	1.230	0.0433
FROM Node16	52	0	4.804	0.648	8.302	0.1135
FROM Node17	46	0	6.100	4.372	24.448	0.1275

experiment18

LINKS: COLLISION STATS

REPLICATION 1 FROM 20.0 TO 240.0 SECONDS

LINK NAME	802.3 CSMA/CD 10BaseT	Link12
ACCESS PROTOCOL	CSMA/CD	CSMA/CD
COLLISION EPISODES	0	0
COLLIDED FRAMES	0	0
NBR OF TRIES TO RESOLVE		
AVERAGE	0.00	0.00
STANDARD DEVIATION	0.00	0.00
MAXIMUM	0	0
NBR OF DEFERRALS	0	0
DEFERRAL DELAY (MS)		
AVERAGE	0.00	0.00
STANDARD DEVIATION	0.00	0.00
MAXIMUM	0.00	0.00
DEFERRAL QUEUE SIZE (FRAMES)		
AVERAGE	0.00	0.00
STANDARD DEVIATION	0.00	0.00
MAXIMUM	0	0
MULTIPLE COLLISION EPISODES		
NBR EPISODES	0	0
AVG PER EPISODE	0.00	0.00
MAX PER EPISODE	0	0

experiment18

MESSAGE + RESPONSE SOURCES: MESSAGE DELIVERED

REPLICATION 1 FROM 20.0 TO 240.0 SECONDS

ORIGIN / MSG SRC NAME: DESTINATION LIST	MESSAGES ASSEMBLED	AVERAGE	MESSAGE DELAY STD DEV	MAXIMUM
Node1 / src e-mail source:				
Node1	5	0.000 MS	0.000 MS	0.000 MS
Node2	10	0.744 MS	0.000 MS	0.744 MS
Node3	3	0.744 MS	0.000 MS	0.744 MS
Node4	5	0.744 MS	0.000 MS	0.744 MS
Node8	6	6.454 MS	0.000 MS	6.454 MS
Node9	5	6.454 MS	0.000 MS	6.454 MS
Node10	5	6.454 MS	0.000 MS	6.454 MS
Node11	1	6.454 MS	0.000 MS	6.454 MS
Node16	6	0.869 MS	0.000 MS	0.869 MS
Node17	5	5.696 MS	0.000 MS	5.696 MS
Node2 / src e-mail responder:				
ECHO	20	2.908 MS	3.204 MS	11.278 MS
Node3 / src WAN e-mail source:				
Node1	3	0.744 MS	0.000 MS	0.744 MS
Node2	6	0.744 MS	0.000 MS	0.744 MS
Node3	4	0.000 MS	0.000 MS	0.000 MS
Node4	9	0.744 MS	0.000 MS	0.744 MS
Node8	8	6.454 MS	0.000 MS	6.454 MS

102

```
                              Stat1.rpt

Node9                    3       6.454 MS       0.000 MS       6.454 MS
Node10                   5       6.454 MS       0.000 MS       6.454 MS
Node11                   4       6.454 MS       0.000 MS       6.454 MS
Node16                   5       0.869 MS       0.000 MS       0.869 MS
Node17                   6       5.696 MS       0.000 MS       5.696 MS
Node8 / src e-mail source:
Node1                    8       6.454 MS       0.000 MS       6.454 MS
Node2                    4       6.454 MS       0.000 MS       6.454 MS
Node3                    6       6.454 MS       0.000 MS       6.454 MS
Node4                    4       6.454 MS       0.000 MS       6.454 MS
Node8                    5       0.000 MS       0.000 MS       0.000 MS
Node9                    4       0.744 MS       0.000 MS       0.744 MS
Node10                   0       0.000 MS       0.000 MS       0.000 MS
Node11                   6       0.744 MS       0.000 MS       0.744 MS
Node16                   6       5.696 MS       0.000 MS       5.696 MS
Node17                   3       0.869 MS       0.000 MS       0.869 MS
Node9 / src e-mail responder:
ECHO                    12       7.990 MS       6.711 MS      23.118 MS
Node10 / src WAN e-mail responder:
ECHO                    10      11.630 MS       9.676 MS      32.618 MS
```

Experiment XIX COMNET III Ethernet Collisions

Primary: _____   Assistant: _____

Signature: _____

Introductory Discussion:

In this experiment you will simulate a 121-node LAN composed of four separate 30-node LAN segments and one 1 server. These five segments are interconnected by a LAN switch. The simulation engine will be used to simulate the message traffic seen on each LAN and through the switch.

Procedure:

This file is already prepared for you in the folder labeled Experiment 19. Note that each LAN has a message source that is different in the mean time between messages generated. This will have a direct effect on the collision statistics that each LAN segment experiences. Use this information to prepare your report on the results. Again, also refer to the desktop image of the simulator.

Questions:

1)   Does the number of messages seen on each LAN agree with what you would expect given the message generation times for each LAN? Show your calculations.

2)   Do the channel utilization statistics agree with what you would expect for the number of collision episodes seen on each LAN? Is the number of collision episodes linear with the channel utilization? How is the relationship you see explained by the MAC layer used in Ethernet?

3)   Compare the collision statistics seen on the server LAN with those of all other LAN segments. What can you conclude from that comparison?

4)   Discuss the results shown in the message and response source delays. How do you reconcile the average message delays with the collision statistics values?

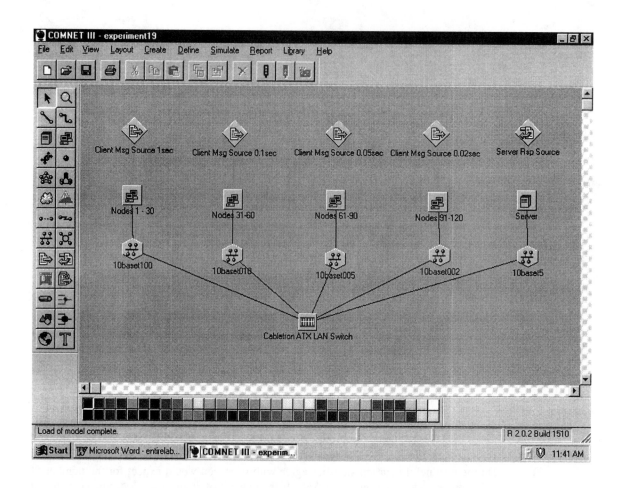

Stat1.rpt

CACI COMNET III Release 2.0.2 Build 1510 Mon May 24 10:12:54 1999   PAGE   1

experiment19

NODES: RECEIVED MESSAGE COUNTS

REPLICATION 1 FROM 20.0 TO 120.0 SECONDS

RECEIVER	COUNT	MESSAGE NAME
Nodes 1 - 30	109	server response msg
Nodes 31-60	1018	server response msg
Nodes 61-90	1989	server response msg
Nodes 91-120	4930	server response msg
Server	4944	0.02 msg source
Server	2000	0.05 msg source
Server	1023	0.1 msg source
Server	109	1 sec msg source

experiment19

LINKS: CHANNEL UTILIZATION

REPLICATION 1 FROM 20.0 TO 120.0 SECONDS

	FRAMES		TRANSMISSION DELAY (MS)			%
LINK	DELIVERED	RST/ERR	AVERAGE	STD DEV	MAXIMUM	UTIL
10baset100	891	0	1.065	0.351	4.503	0.9387
10baset010	8348	0	1.093	0.488	19.954	8.8113
10baset005	16279	0	1.122	0.748	40.814	17.14
10baset002	40402	0	1.286	2.458	158.588	42.62
10baset5	65877	0	1.659	10.419	1258.342	69.50

CACI COMNET III Release 2.0.2 Build 1510 Mon May 24 10:12:54 1999 PAGE 3

experiment19

LINKS: FRAME SIZE

REPLICATION 1 FROM 20.0 TO 120.0 SECONDS

		FRAME SIZES (BYTES)		
LINK	COUNT	AVERAGE	STD DEV	MAXIMUM
10baset100	891	1316.930	413.336	1526.000
10baset010	8348	1319.372	407.149	1526.000
10baset005	16279	1316.093	411.449	1526.000
10baset002	40402	1318.745	407.545	1526.000
10baset5	65877	1318.665	408.171	1526.000

experiment19

LINKS: COLLISION STATS

REPLICATION 1 FROM 20.0 TO 120.0 SECONDS

LINK NAME	10baset100	10baset010	10baset005	10baset002
ACCESS PROTOCOL	CSMA/CD	CSMA/CD	CSMA/CD	CSMA/CD
COLLISION EPISODES	4	214	763	5089
COLLIDED FRAMES	8	428	1526	10178
NBR OF TRIES TO RESOLVE				
AVERAGE	2.00	1.67	1.69	1.73
STANDARD DEVIATION	1.22	1.27	1.35	1.56
MAXIMUM	4	8	9	15
NBR OF DEFERRALS	3	251	891	5725
DEFERRAL DELAY (MS)				
AVERAGE	0.97	0.64	0.68	0.68
STANDARD DEVIATION	0.21	0.39	0.38	0.38
MAXIMUM	1.12	1.22	1.22	1.22
DEFERRAL QUEUE SIZE (FRAMES)				
AVERAGE	0.00	0.00	0.01	0.04
STANDARD DEVIATION	0.01	0.04	0.08	0.19
MAXIMUM	1	1	1	1

MULTIPLE COLLISION EPISODES
NBR EPISODES   0   0   0
AVG PER EPISODE   0.00   0.00   0.00
MAX PER EPISODE   0   0   0

CACI COMNET III Release 2.0.2 Build 1510 Mon May 24 10:12:54 1999   PAGE   5

experiment19

LINKS: COLLISION STATS

REPLICATION 1 FROM 20.0 TO 120.0 SECONDS

LINK NAME   10baset5

ACCESS PROTOCOL   CSMA/CD

COLLISION EPISODES   16577

COLLIDED FRAMES   33154

NBR OF TRIES TO RESOLVE
AVERAGE   1.82
STANDARD DEVIATION   1.81
MAXIMUM   16

NBR OF DEFERRALS   15724

DEFERRAL DELAY   (MS)
    AVERAGE   0.69
    STANDARD DEVIATION   0.37
    MAXIMUM   1.22

DEFERRAL QUEUE SIZE   (FRAMES)
    AVERAGE   0.11
    STANDARD DEVIATION   0.31
    MAXIMUM   1

MULTIPLE COLLISION EPISODES
    NBR EPISODES   0
    AVG PER EPISODE   0.00
    MAX PER EPISODE   0

experiment19

MESSAGE + RESPONSE SOURCES: MESSAGE DELIVERED

REPLICATION 1 FROM 20.0 TO 120.0 SECONDS

ORIGIN / MSG SRC NAME: DESTINATION LIST	MESSAGES ASSEMBLED	AVERAGE	MESSAGE DELAY STD DEV	MAXIMUM
Nodes 1 - 30 / src Client Msg Source 1sec:				
Server	109	58.918 MS	183.256 MS	1251.624 MS
Nodes 31-60 / src Client Msg Source 0.1sec:				
Server	1023	49.992 MS	167.943 MS	1225.837 MS
Nodes 61-90 / src Client Msg Source 0.05sec:				
Server	2000	45.830 MS	154.511 MS	1258.804 MS
Nodes 91-120 / src Client Msg Source 0.02sec:				
Server	4944	50.546 MS	162.411 MS	1250.187 MS
Server / src Server Rsp Source:				
ECHO	8046	55.557 MS	123.202 MS	988.824 MS

Experiment XX COMNET III Modem Pool

Primary: _____   Assistant: _____

Signature: _____

Introductory Discussion:

In this experiment you will simulate a modem pool that is used by the clients to dial up the server. There are four V.90 modems in the pool configured for a 33.6 kbps up-link to the pool and 53 kbps downlink from the pool. Each modem has several parameters set that you will vary and experimentally determine the impact. The default setup is a connect delay of 2 seconds and a disconnect delay of 1 second. Each modem features a frame error rate of 1 error in 1,000,000 frames. Additionally, the retry time is initially set to 10 seconds. These parameters are saved in myparamset in the link type parameters of the modem pool icon.

Procedure:

This file is already prepared for you in the folder labeled Experiment 20. During the simulation the modem pool responds to client nodes if there is a modem available. Each modem behaves like a separate dialup with its own delay for connecting and disconnecting and a retry time if no modem is available.

Questions:

Vary the modem pool and server parameters as follows and report your results.

1)   The number of modems in the pool is intially set to eight, one for each client. After running the simulation configured as it is, change the number of modems to 6 and then 4. Discuss your results.

2)   The error rate is initially set to 1 error in 1,000,000 frames. Change this to 1 error in 1,000 frames and discuss your results. Was there any significant change? Why?

3)   Change the message size calculation probability distribution of the server from NOR(1000,100) to NOR(10000,1000), increasing the server response message size by a factor of 10. What impacts occurred? Why?

4)   Change the time to connect from 2 seconds to 10 seconds. What impact did you observe?

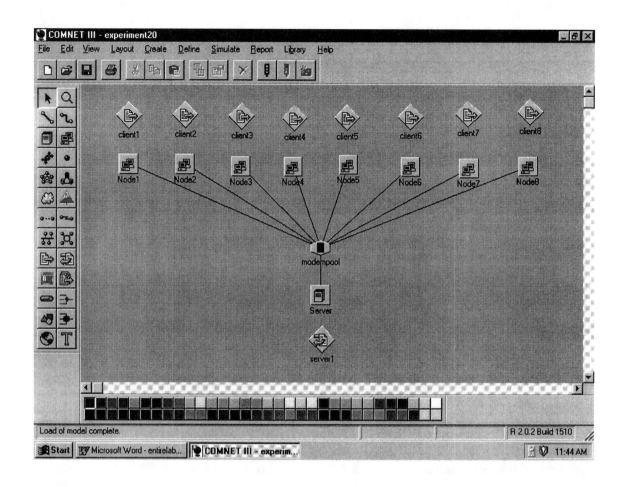

stat1.rpt

CACI COMNET III Release 2.0.2 Build 1510 Sun May 30 10:01:03 1999 PAGE 1

experiment20

NODES: RECEIVED MESSAGE COUNTS

REPLICATION 1 FROM 10.0 TO 110.0 SECONDS

RECEIVER	COUNT	MESSAGE NAME
Node1	18	server response
Node2	23	server response
Node3	23	server response
Server	16	client6
Server	20	client7
Server	15	client4
Server	19	client8
Server	18	client1
Server	23	client2
Server	23	client3
Server	19	client5
Node4	15	server response
Node5	19	server response
Node6	16	server response
Node7	20	server response
Node8	19	server response

CACI COMNET III Release 2.0.2 Build 1510 Sun May 30 10:01:03 1999 PAGE 2

experiment20

LINKS: CHANNEL UTILIZATION

REPLICATION 1 FROM 10.0 TO 110.0 SECONDS

| | FRAMES | | TRANSMISSION DELAY (MS) | | | % |
LINK	DELIVERED RST/ERR		AVERAGE	STD DEV	MAXIMUM	UTIL
modempool	153	0	131.656	59.358	237.381	20.14
modempool	153	0	151.542	16.415	189.585	23.19

CACI COMNET III Release 2.0.2 Build 1510 Sun May 30 10:01:03 1999 PAGE 3

experiment20

LINKS: LINK CONNECTION STATS

REPLICATION 1 FROM 10.0 TO 110.0 SECONDS

| | BUSY CONNECTIONS | | | CONNECTION DELAY (MS) | | |
LINK	MAX	MEAN	SDEV	MEAN	STD DEV	MAXIMUM
modempool	8	0.00	0.00	0.000	0.000	0.000

experiment20

MESSAGE + RESPONSE SOURCES: MESSAGE DELIVERED

REPLICATION 1 FROM 10.0 TO 110.0 SECONDS

ORIGIN / MSG SRC NAME: DESTINATION LIST	MESSAGES ASSEMBLED	AVERAGE	MESSAGE DELAY STD DEV	MAXIMUM
Node1 / src client1:				
Server	18	145.331 MS	57.789 MS	235.238 MS
Node2 / src client2:				
Server	23	155.611 MS	63.628 MS	226.667 MS
Node3 / src client3:				
Server	23	127.061 MS	55.345 MS	228.571 MS
Server / src server1:				
ECHO	153	152.483 MS	19.033 MS	251.506 MS
Node4 / src client4:				
Server	15	118.032 MS	49.292 MS	215.714 MS
Node5 / src client5:				
Server	19	125.201 MS	55.449 MS	237.143 MS
Node6 / src client6:				
Server	16	135.830 MS	64.945 MS	230.952 MS
Node7 / src client7:				
Server	20	113.774 MS	58.410 MS	237.143 MS
Node8 / src client8:				
Server	19	128.459 MS	54.536 MS	237.381 MS